# The Great British Songbook

**Wise Publications**
part of The Music Sales Group
London/New York/Paris/Sydney/Copenhagen/Berlin/Madrid/Hong Kong/Tokyo

Published by
**Wise Publications**
14-15 Berners Street,
London W1T 3LJ, UK.

Exclusive Distributors:
**Music Sales Limited**
Distribution Centre,
Newmarket Road,
Bury St Edmunds,
Suffolk IP33 3YB, UK.

Order No. AM1005312
ISBN 978-1-78038-706-2

This book © Copyright 2006
Wise Publications,
a division of Music Sales Limited.

New arrangements and engraving
supplied by Camden Music.

Music edited by Christopher Harvey.

Song notes by Philip Glassborow
and Graham Vickers.

Book design by Stephen Coates.

Picture research by Dave Brolan.

Photographs courtesy of Corbis.
Getty Images. London Features
International. Chris Walter/
Photofeatures. Pictorial Press.
Jorgen Angel, Dick Barnatt, Fin
Costello, Ian Dickson, Harry
Goodwin, Tom Hanley, Hayley
Madden, Gered Mankowitz,
Martin O'Neill, David Redfern, Ebet
Roberts, Virginia Turbett/Redferns.
Eugene Adebari, Dezo Hoffmann,
Alan Messer, Brian Rasic, Ray
Stevenson, Richard Young/Rex
Features. Nicholas Burnham, David
Corio, Steve Double, Spiros Politis,
Michael Putland, Mick Young/
Retna. Ed Sirrs. Joe McGorty/
stemagency.com. Adrian Boot/
urbanimage.tv. Robert Whitaker.

Compiled by Nick Crispin.

Printed in the EU.

**Your Guarantee of Quality**

As publishers, we strive to produce
every book to the highest
commercial standards.
This book has been carefully
designed to minimise awkward
page turns and to make playing
from it a real pleasure.

Particular care has been given to
specifying acid-free, neutral-sized
paper made from pulps which
have not been elemental chlorine
bleached.

This pulp is from farmed
sustainable forests and was
produced with special regard for
the environment. Throughout,
the printing and binding have
been planned to ensure a sturdy,
attractive publication which
should give years of enjoyment.
If your copy fails to meet our high
standards, please inform us and we
will gladly replace it.

**www.musicsales.com**

# Contents

# Contents

# HEY JUDE
## BY JOHN LENNON & PAUL McCARTNEY

Photograph by John Kelly / Stephen Goldblatt

# NORTHERN SONGS LIMITED

3/.

In the beginning
was the word.
And God said,
Let there be noise

And there was noise.

There was silence,
then there was a word,
then there was sound.

And God eventually,
after a bit of prevaricating,
found a way for it all to be
recorded.

From *Words And Music: A History of Pop* by Paul Morley

# Introduction

In 1952, the optimistic year that Elizabeth became queen, British popular music was in need of a new direction. The once vigorous domestic influences of music hall and variety were gone but an enduring alliance between mainstream show business and popular music still prevailed. Some music publishers had themselves become songwriters, bridging the two disciplines, and — not unreasonably — feeling confident that they could ride all foreseeable waves of changing musical tastes. After all, it was all show business, wasn't it?

In fact it wasn't. White rock 'n' roll was being born in the USA and it was addressing a new demographic: a youth audience with tastes of its own and no time for the comfortable accommodations of the old Tin Pan Alley or the model of the all-round entertainer who closed his or her stage act with a song. Elvis Presley, Bill Haley, Jerry Lee Lewis et al heralded a new order and duly inspired their own British imitators. Britain was still in post-war austerity and its youth was yet to achieve the degree of financial independence that would follow. There was, though, another obstacle to American rock's trip across the Atlantic. It presented British pop singers with a paradox: how to sing American-style music credibly with a British accent? The Beatles would eventually provide the answer (but, like their rivals The Rolling Stones, only after slavishly imitating a number of American records to begin with). Eventually though the Brits would be able to sell back to the Americans their own property…except that by now it was no longer their own property, belonging, as it did, to much of the world's youth. From the 1960s onwards British song writing and recording would fully embrace and absorb American rock and its offshoots, and it managed to do so without sounding like a pale imitation. A common language helped, but it was Britain more than anywhere else that developed the most distinctive domestic strand of non-American rock, eventually feeding back into it some of the Celtic roots music that had formed one of the strands of early American rock 'n' roll.

More exotic influences would follow and they too would be assimilated into British songs: Jamaican and Indian music were absorbed to run alongside the ancient indigenous Irish, Scottish and Welsh musical traditions. As the Commonwealth shrank, former colonies began once again to be culturally identified through their traditional music. In parallel, British songs found room for unashamedly English rockers who celebrated a quirky, vernacular Britishness — witness the songs of Ray Davies, Ian Dury, Richard Thompson and Jarvis Cocker. As this volume so vividly demonstrates, there is always room for variety in the Great British Songbook. Romantic songs of longing and fulfilment still abound, but so do songs that wear their musical cross-references and

multicultural influences lightly. And, like death and taxes, the novelty song is always with us, a phenomenon which inexplicably catches the public fancy and, in its own eccentric way, offers further proof that the British song writing is not just still alive, it is in rude health.

The British popular music charts were introduced in 1952, the same year as Elizabeth acceded to the throne. American records dominated those early charts but gradually the pattern began to change. Today the once unheard of feat of British songs topping the American charts is commonplace. And today there will even be official pop music events as part of the 2012 Diamond Jubilee celebrations, an unimaginably frivolous concept back in a post-war Britain defined by ration books, bomb sites and a strictly non-populist royal family. These 2012 Jubilee music events will be broadcast in HD, 3D and multi-channel stereo, then packaged and marketed as music products in their own right. In stark contrast, broadcast TV was a still a fledgling thing when Elizabeth became queen and she became one of its first stars when her 1953 Coronation was shown across those bits of the land that could receive anything at all on flickering 9-inch black-and-white sets owned by relatively few households and into whose living rooms neighbours were crammed so as to share in this exciting confluence of new technology and royal ceremony. Those two starkly contrasting points in Britain's social history form neat bookends to the 60 years of popular music represented in the following pages. Of course, that music was only part of many seismic cultural upheavals that took place between then and now, but, as ever, it was perhaps the music that best reflected back to the British people what was on their minds and in their hearts.

# Mud, mud, glorious mud;

nothing quite like it for cooling the blood.
So follow me, follow,
down to the hollow,
and there let us wallow in glorious mud.

Among their beloved revue numbers, Michael Flanders, left, and Donald Swann, right, enjoyed particular success with a veritable bestiary of animal songs. 'The Rhinoceros', 'The Elephant', 'The Warthog' and a brace of G-nu ("I'm a G-nu… a-g-nother g-nu!") were favourites of many a radio programme in the fifties and sixties. Yet perhaps their most enduring creation was 'The

Hippopotamus' with its rousing refrain which generations of school-children have rejoiced in singing. This was the song that put mud on the musical map, long before Glastonbury. According to the publishers, it has been translated into many languages including French, German, Russian, Icelandic, Indonesian and Welsh.

Appropriately, Michael Flanders also wrote the libretto for the

children's cantata 'Captain Noah And The Floating Zoo'. Donald Swann's other compositions include settings of works by Tolkien and Sydney Carter as well as carols and psalms. Together, they performed their songs in revues like At The Drop Of A Hat, and their best-selling LPs (recorded in front of a live theatre audience) were produced by a pre-Beatles George Martin.

# 1952

# The Hippopotamus

Words & Music by Michael Flanders & Donald Swann
© Copyright 1952 Chappell Music Limited.
All Rights Reserved. International Copyright Secured.

(Verses 2 & 3 see block lyrics)

*Verse 2:*

The fair hippopotama he aimed to entice,
From her seat on that hilltop above.
As she hadn't got a ma to give her advice,
Came tiptoeing down to her love.
Like thunder the forest re-echoed the sound
Of the song that they sang as they met.
His inamorata adjusted her garter,
And lifted her voice in duet...

*Verse 3:*

Now, more hippopotami began to convene
On the banks of that river so wide.
I wonder, now what am I to say of the scene
That ensued by the Shalimar side.
They dived all at once with an ear-splitting splosh,
Then rose to the surface again.
A regular army of hippopotami,
All singing this haunting refrain...

I know I could be happy with you, my darling, if you could be happy with me.

# I Could Be Happy With You

Words & Music by Sandy Wilson
© Copyright 1953 Chappell Music Limited.
All Rights Reserved. International Copyright Secured.

# 1954

# The Dam Busters March

Music by Eric Coates
© Copyright 1954 Chappell Music Limited.
All Rights Reserved. International Copyright Secured.

# 1956

# Nellie The Elephant

Words by Ralph Butler
Music by Peter Hart
© Copyright 1956 Dash Music Company Limited.
All Rights Reserved. International Copyright Secured.

Off she went with a trumpety trump, trump, trump, trump.

# 1956

# The Ying Tong Song

Words & Music by Spike Milligan
© Copyright 1956 Spike Milligan.
All Rights Reserved. International Copyright Secured.

ying tong id - dle - i - po.    Ying tong ying tong ying tong id - dle - i - po,    id - dle - i - po.    Oo.

*Verse 2:*

Ying, ying tongy tongy, ying tong iddle-i-po, ying tong iddle-i-po, ying, ying, ying tongy tongy.

Ying, ying tong, ying tongy yingy po, ying tong ticky, tick-tick-ticky, ying tong iddle-i-po.

Hear that crazy rhythm driving me insane.

Strike your partner on the bonce. *(Thump)* Oo, I felt no pain!

The *Goon Show* was a landmark BBC radio series starring Spike Milligan, Harry Secombe and Peter Sellers, which ran from 1951 to 1960. "The show did not so much push back the frontiers of radio comedy as trample them underfoot," according to Goon historian Roger Wilmut. Yet entwined within the show's surreal, anarchic humour – and delight in silly voices and catch-phrases – there was also a strong undercurrent of music. Mainly jazz. The shows featured musical interludes from harmonica virtuoso Max Geldray and from Ray Ellington's Quartet, as well as the signature theme and music links from Wally Stott and His Orchestra. (British music legend Wally Stott also composed the signature tune

for another much-loved radio comedy series, *Hancock's Half Hour*.)

Occasionally the Goon characters themselves would break into song (well, they had to break in, they couldn't find the key!)... and some of these extraordinary numbers were released as 78rpm records. They included 'I'm Walking Backwards For Christmas' (originally performed in a *Goon Show* broadcast by Spike Milligan) and 'Bloodnok's Rock And Roll Call' with its B-side 'The Ying Tong Song', featuring Maurice Ponke and his Orchestre Fromage. (When re-released in 1973, 'The Ying Tong Song' spent five weeks in the charts, peaking at number nine in the Top Ten.)

*The Goon Show's* influence has been acknowledged by countless

comedians and musicians – among them John Lennon, who reviewed a collection of Goon Show scripts for *The New York Times*:

"I was twelve when the *Goon Shows* first hit me. Sixteen when they were finished with me. Their humour was the only proof that the world was insane. As they say in Tibet, 'You had to be there.' The Goons influenced The Beatles (along with Lewis Carroll/Elvis Presley). Before becoming The Beatles' producer, George Martin, who had never recorded rock 'n' roll, had previously recorded with Milligan and Sellers, which made him all the more acceptable – our studio sessions were full of the cries of Neddie Seagoon, etc., etc., as were most places in Britain...

*The Goon Show* was long before

and more revolutionary than *Look Back In Anger* (it appealed to 'eggheads' and 'the people'). Hipper than the hippest and madder than *Mad*, a conspiracy against reality. A *coup d'etat* of the mind! P.S. Dick Lester (of *A Hard Day's Night* fame) directed the TV version of the *Goon Show - A Show Called Fred*."

Another celebrated fan of the series was HRH Prince Charles, who wrote in 1973: "No matter how much fashion in humour changes, there will always be thousands of people whose minds are attuned to the kind of mental slapstick and imaginary cartoonery that typifies Goonery."

The Goons, clockwise from left, Spike Milligan, Peter Sellers, Ian Carmichael, Harry Secombe & Michael Bentine

# 1959 | Apache

Music by Jerry Lordan
© Copyright 1959 Francis Day & Hunter Limited.
All Rights Reserved. International Copyright Secured.

# Living Doll

Words & Music by Lionel Bart
© Copyright 1959 Peter Maurice Music Company Limited.
All Rights Reserved. International Copyright Secured.

Got a **roving eye** and that is why she satisfies my soul.

# Where Is Love?

Words & Music by Lionel Bart
© Copyright 1959 Lakeview Music Publishing Company Limited.
All Rights Reserved. International Copyright Secured.

**Slowly, but rhythmically**

Where is love? Does it fall from skies a - bove?

Is it un - der - neath the wil - low tree that I've been dream - ing of?

Where is she, who I close my eyes to see?

Will I ev - er know the sweet "hel - lo" that's meant for on - ly me?

Who can say where she may hide? Must I trav - el far and wide, till I am be - side the

some - one who I can mean some - thing to? Where,

**1.** where is love?

**2.** *rit.* love?

## Where is love?

# Does it come from skies above?

### Is it underneath the willow tree that I've been dreaming of?

Lionel Bart, above, had written pop hits for Tommy Steele and Cliff Richard (see 'Living Doll' on page 53), and had also shown considerable promise in musical theatre with *Fings Ain't Wot They Used To Be*. But nothing had prepared London (or indeed the world) for his masterly musical adaptation of *Oliver Twist*. Renamed *Oliver!* – and starring the great Ron Moody as Fagin – it was filled with gusto and melody: everything from show-stoppers like 'Consider Yourself', 'I'd Do Anything' and 'Food, Glorious Food', to tender ballads like 'As Long As He Needs Me' and 'Where Is Love?' The show triumphed in the West End and the sumptuous movie version, again starring Ron Moody, won five Academy Awards including the Oscar for Best Picture.

# My Old Man's A Dustman

Words & Music by Lonnie Donegan,
Peter Buchanan & Beverly Thorn
© Copyright 1960 Tyler Music Limited.
All Rights Reserved. International Copyright Secured.

**Lively**

*ad lib.*

1. Now here's a lit-tle stor-y, to tell it____ is a must, a-

-bout an un-sung he-ro, that moves a-way your dust. Some

peop-le make a for-tune, oth-ers earn a mint;

**rit.**

my old man don't earn much, in fact he's flip-pin' skint! Oh!

**A tempo** ♩ = 128

My old man's a dust-man, he wears a dust-man's hat, he

wears cor blim-ey trous-ers, and he lives in a coun-cil flat. He

looks a pro-per 'na - na in his great big hob-nail boots. He's

got such a job to pull them up that he calls them dais-y roots. 2. Some

folks give tips at Christ-mas, and some of them__ for - get, so
*(Verses 3,4,5 see block lyric)*

when he picks their bins up, he spills some on the step. Now

one old man got nast - y and to the coun - cil wrote. Next

time my old man went round there he punched him up the throat. Oh!

My old man's a dust - man he wears a dust - man's hat, he

wears cor blim - ey trous - ers, and he lives in a coun - cil flat. (Next)

*4th time only*

**1, 2, 3.**   **4.**

G (Vamp until ready)

(Spoken interludes) time you see a dust-man, look-ing all pale and sad, Don't kick him in___ the

dust - bin, it might be my old dad._____

*1st spoken interlude:*
I say, I say, Les
Yeah?
I found a police dog in my dustbin,
Well how do you know it was a police dog?
He had a policeman with him!

*2nd spoken interlude:*
I say, I say, I say,
Yeah?
My dustbin's full of lillies,
Well, throw them away then!
I can't, Lilly's wearing them!

*Verse 3:*
Though my old man's a dustman, he's got a heart of gold,
He got married recently, though he's eighty-six years old,
We said "Here, hang on Dad, you're getting past your prime!",
He said "Well, when you get to my age, it helps to pass the time!"

*Verse 4:*
Now one day when in a hurry, he missed a lady's bin,
He hadn't gone but a few yards when she chased after him,
"What game do you think you're playing?", she cried right from the heart,
"You've missed me, am I too late?", "No, jump up on the cart!"

*3rd spoken interlude:*
I say, I say, I say.
What, you again?
My dustbin's absolutely full with toadstools,
How do you know it's full,
Because there's not 'mush-room' inside!

*Verse 5:*
He found a tiger's head one day, nailed to a piece of wood,
The tiger looked quite miserable, but I suppose he should,
Just then, from out a window, a voice began to wail, he said, "Oi, where's me tiger's head?"
"Four foot from his tail!"

With lyrics by Robert Mellin and music by traditional jazz clarinettist Mr. Acker Bilk, right, (Bilk claimed to have adopted the 'Mr.' as a democratic equivalent of the self-styled Dukes and Counts of the modern jazz world) this song has a unique history. It was first heard on BBC TV in September of 1961 as an instrumental theme tune to a now forgotten drama about a young Frenchwoman coming to Britain. Bilk had originally written and named the melody for his daughter Jenny, but it became 'Stranger On The Shore' and was a hit not only in Britain but also in America where, on May 26, 1962, it was the first ever British recording to reach number one on the Billboard Hot 100.

# 1961 | Stranger On The Shore

Music by Acker Bilk
© Copyright 1961 Sherwin Music Company (London)/
EMI Music Publishing Limited.
All Rights Reserved. International Copyright Secured.

# The Young Ones

Words & Music by Roy Bennett &
Sid Tepper
© Copyright 1961 EMI Film & Theatre Music Limited.
All Rights Reserved. International Copyright Secured.

**Verse 2:**

Tomorrow, why wait until tomorrow?
'Cause tomorrow sometimes never comes.
So leave me, there's a song to be sung,
And the best time is to sing it while we're young.

Let us not forget that Cliff Richard was making pop movies even before The Beatles. Hollywood, with its mighty studio resources and unlimited sunshine, had beach movies, rock 'n' roll and Elvis. So, with tuppence-halfpenny in the budget but Heath Robinson ingenuity, Britain fought back with Cliff. Following a surprisingly astringent 1959 comment on coffee-bar culture, *Expresso Bongo* (adapted from Wolf Mankowitz's West End musical), Cliff starred in three joyfully escapist pop films. The most enduring were *The Young Ones*, with Melvyn Hayes for comedy relief, and *Summer Holiday*, with Melvyn Hayes again plus a red double-decker bus, and – best of all for pop fans – Cliff's real-life backing group, The Shadows (see the note on 'Apache' on page 52). Some film buffs bravely maintain that the Cliff Richard movies were just as influential on the later genre of pop videos as Dick Lester's films for The Beatles. They were certainly good clean fun, featuring genial comedy, exuberant choreography (from a pre-Cats Gillian Lynne among others) and an eclectic mix of songs. Some of them, like this number, were from imported Tin Pan Alley writers, but many were home-grown hits.

The title song of *The Young Ones*, a cheery pop number, would later become the title of an anarchic, shambolic TV comedy series, and Cliff gamely joined in with the TV cast to record a charity single. 'The Young Ones' was also among the medley of his greatest hits that Sir Cliff famously performed, spontaneously, for a delighted sing-along audience at Wimbledon when rain stopped play. And you don't get more British than that!

Film students in search of a PhD subject might do worse than investigate "Pre-and-post-Beatle British pop films." *Play It Cool* (1962) featured Billy Fury and Helen Shapiro. *It's Trad, Dad* (1962, directed by a pre-Beatle Dick Lester) mingled British pop stars with trad-jazz players Acker Bilk and Kenny Ball, along with a tranche of US guest acts including Chubby Checker and Gene Vincent. *Just For Fun* (1962, cinematography by Nicolas Roeg) featured Joe Meek's stable of stars including The Tornados (see the entry on 'Telstar', page 66) plus Brian Poole and the Tremeloes, Kenny Lynch, and the three reigning disc-jockeys of that era, David Jacobs, Alan Freeman and Jimmy Savile. And then everyone got into the act: Joe Brown in *What A Crazy World*… Herman's Hermits in *Mrs. Brown, You've Got A Lovely Daughter*… the Dave Clark Five in *Catch Us If You Can*… and Gerry and the Pacemakers in *Ferry 'Cross The Mersey*.

Below (L-R): Hank Marvin, Tony Meehan, Cliff & Bruce Welch.

# Tomorrow, why wait until tomorrow?
### 'Cause tomorrow sometimes never comes.

# 1962

# Island Of Dreams

Words & Music by Tom Springfield
© Copyright 1962 Springfield Music Limited.
Chappell Music Limited.
All Rights Reserved. International Copyright Secured.

**With a hillbilly swing!** ♩ = 124

High in the sky is a bird on a wing; please carry me with you.

# 1962 Right Said Fred

Words by Myles Rudge
Music by Ted Dicks
© Copyright 1962 Noel Gay Music Company Limited.
All Rights Reserved. International Copyright Secured.

Lively ♩ = 100

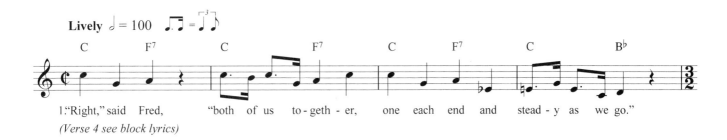

1:"Right," said Fred, "both of us to-geth-er, one each end and stead-y as we go."
*(Verse 4 see block lyrics)*

Tried to shift it, could-n't e-ven lift it, we was get-ting

no-where, and so we had a cup of tea and... 2."Right," said Fred,
*(Verse 5 see block lyrics)*

"give a shout for Char-lie", up comes Char-lie, from the floor bel-ow.

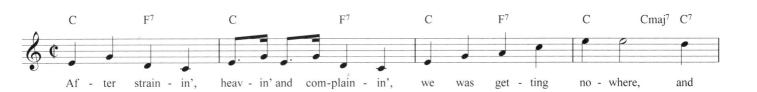

Af-ter strain-in', heav-in' and com-plain-in', we was get-ting no-where, and

so we had a cup of tea and... Char-lie 'ad a think and he thought we ought to
*(Bridge 2 see block lyrics)*

take off all the 'an-dles, and the things what 'eld the can-dles. But it

Whatever happened to Larky Songs? Back in those lazy, hazy, crazy days of summer – just before the sixties really started swinging – pop was fun! The airwaves were awash with variety. Cheek by jowl with rock 'n' rollers were crooners and chanteuses, skifflers and siffleurs: a mardi-gras melee of Luxembourg and Light Programme favourites. And a young record producer called George Martin – yes, the 'fifth Beatle' himself! – was cornering the market in recorded humour.

"I started in comedy really because I had nowhere else to go," Sir George recalled recently. "I was running the Parlophone label, and the big boys – HMV, Columbia, RCA – had all the major stars. We couldn't compete, so I had to try and do something different."

Thus, at the not-yet-legendary Abbey Road studios (or occasionally in front of a 'live' theatre audience), George Martin was making comedy records with Peter Sellers, Peter Ustinov, Flanders & Swann (see page 43), Spike Milligan (see page 50), and another soon-to-be Fab Foursome, the "Beyond The Fringe" team. (Two of whom, Peter Cook and Dudley Moore, are represented on page 87.)

Among George Martin's biggest comedy hits were two singles by Bernard Cribbins, below, written by Myles Rudge and Ted Dicks: 'The Hole In The Ground' and 'Right Said Fred,' which both charted in the Top Ten.

Dicks & Rudge went on to write many more Larky Songs, including that perennial singalong favourite about a little mouse with clogs on, 'A Windmill In Old Amsterdam'. Sadly, in today's MTV world, the novelty number has more or less vanished from view. Now the terrain is overrun by those voracious predators – Rock, Pop, Rap – it seems as if all the Larky Songs are hiding in the undergrowth, like wary deer.

Sir George Martin blames TV: "I think the fun element in music stopped with television, because people started listening with their eyes instead of their ears." It's a shame that today's young listeners no longer have access on the airwaves to the Larky as well as the funky, the Quirky as well as the cool...

Tried to shift it, couldn't even lift it, we was getting nowhere,

and so we had a cup of tea...

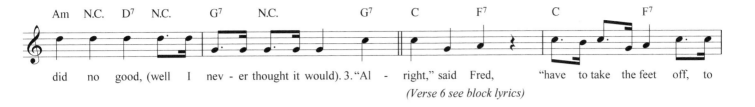

did    no    good, (well    I    nev - er thought it would). 3."Al - right," said Fred,    "have    to take the feet    off,    to

*(Verse 6 see block lyrics)*

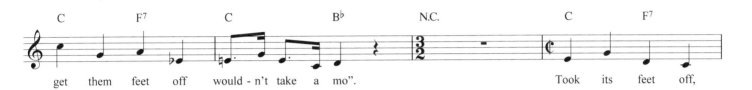

get    them    feet    off    would - n't take    a    mo".    Took    its    feet    off,

e - ven    took    the    seat    off,    should    have    got    us    some - where,    but    no!_____

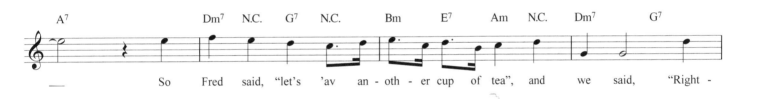

___    So    Fred    said,    "let's    'av    an - oth - er    cup    of    tea",    and    we    said,    "Right -

- o!"    *Spoken:* I said to Charlie, "We'll have to leave it standing on the landing, that's all.
You see the trouble with Fred is he's too hasty. You never get nowhere if you're too hasty!"

*Verse 4:*
"Right," said Fred, "'ave to take the door off,
Need more space to shift the so-and-so."
'Ad bad twinges taking off the 'inges,
And it got us nowhere, and so we had a cup of tea and...

*Verse 5:*
"Right," said Fred, "'ave to take the wall down,
That there wall is going to have to go."
Took the wall down, even with it all down,
We were getting nowhere, and so we had a cup of tea.

*Bridge 2:*
And Charlie had a think and he said, "Look, Fred,
I've got a sort of feeling,
If we remove the ceiling,
With a rope or two, we could drop the blighter through."

*Verse 6:*
"Alright," said Fred, climbing up a ladder,
With his crowbar gave a mighty blow.
Was he in trouble, 'alf a ton of rubble,
Landed on top of his dome.
So Charlie and me had another cup of tea,
And then we went home.

# 1962 | Telstar

Music by Joe Meek
© Copyright 1962 Ivy Music Limited.
All Rights Reserved. International Copyright Secured.

Decades before "home recording" became commonplace, Joe Meek produced many pioneering hit songs in his flat above a shop in London's Holloway Road. John Leyton recalls the recording session for 'Johnny Remember Me': "The string section was up the stairs, the backing vocalists were in the bathroom [for added echo!], I was in the sitting room and Joe was in the kitchen." However, it was the space-age instrumental 'Telstar' that rocket-propelled Meek to international success, with some highly impressive statistics. He was Britain's first independent record producer... his record topped not only the British but also the American charts... and The Tornados, Meek's "house" band (literally!), were the first British pop group to have a US Number One.

In the years following his sensational death in 1967 – he shot his landlady before killing himself – Joe Meek has become a cult figure, with fan-clubs, websites, books and a stage play about his life. Among the retrospectives of his legacy, his 1960 concept album, *I Hear A New World*, using experimental techniques of tape delay, looping and stereo, was finally released a few years ago... some three decades after it was produced.

# Flash, Bang, Wallop!

Words & Music by David Heneker
© Copyright 1963 Britannia Music Company Limited.
Chappell Music Limited.
All Rights Reserved. International Copyright Secured.

**With energy**

1. All lined up in a wed-ding group, here we are for a pho-to-graph,_ we're
(Verse 2 see block lyrics)
all dressed up in a morn-ing suit all try-ing not to laugh._ Since the ear-ly cave-man
in his fur_ took a trip to Gret-na Green, there's al-ways been a pho-to - graph-er_ to rec-
-ord the hap-py scene. Oh yeah, flash, bang, wall-op what a pic-ture, click, what a pic-ture,
what a pho-to-graph. Poor old soul, bli-mey what a joke, hat blown off in a cloud of smoke! Clap your
hands, stamp your feet,_ bang-ing on the big bass drum. What a pic-ture,
what a pic-ture, um, tid-dle-y um, pum, pum, pum, pum! Stick it in your fam-'ly al-bum!

**1.**

**2.**

You've read it in a fo-li-o_ or
seen it in a Shakes-peare play, how Jul-i-et fell for Ro-me-o_ in the mer-ry_ month of
May. And as he climbed the orch-ard wall to reach his la-dy fair, as he

*Verse 2:*

The same thing happened long ago when man was in his prime,
And what went on we only know from the snaps he took at the time,
When Adam and Eve in their birthday suit decided to get wed,
As Adam was about to taste the fruit,
The man with the camera said:

*Chorus:*

Hold it, flash, bang, wallop, what a picture,
Click, what a picture, what a photograph,
Poor old Eve, there with nothing on,
Face all red with the fig leaf gone,
Clap your hands *etc.*

Clap your hands, stamp your feet, **banging** on the big bass drum.

Tommy Steele

# 1963

# I Only Want To Be With You

Words & Music by Mike Hawker & Ivor Raymonde
© Copyright 1963 Chappell Music Limited.
All Rights Reserved. International Copyright Secured.

**With a bounce** ♩ = 132

1. I don't know what it is that makes me love you so,___ I on-ly know I nev-er want to

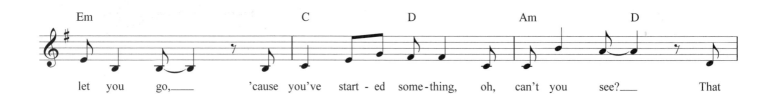

let you go,___ 'cause you've start-ed some-thing, oh, can't you see?___ That

ev-er since we met you've had a hold on me,___ it hap-pens to be true,___ I

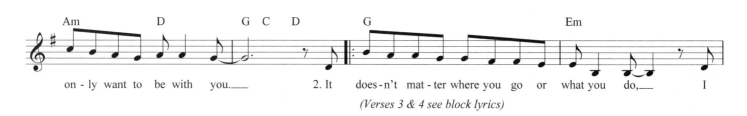

on-ly want to be with you.___ 2. It does-n't mat-ter where you go or what you do,___ I

*(Verses 3 & 4 see block lyrics)*

want to spend each mo-ment of the day with you,___ oh, look what has hap-pened with just one kiss,___ I

nev-er knew that I could be in love like this,___ it's craz-y but it's true,___ I

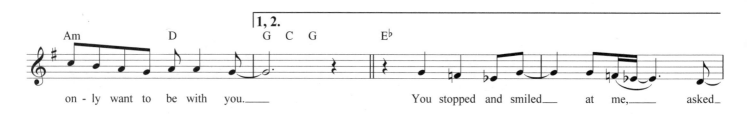

on-ly want to be with you.___ You stopped and smiled___ at me,___ asked___

_ if I cared_ to_ dance._ I_ fell in_ to your op - en arms,_ and I did - n't stand a chance_ now list - en hon - ey! _ I said no

**3.**

mat - ter no mat - ter what_ you do,_ I on - ly want to be with you._

_Verses 3 & 4:_

I just want to be beside you everywhere,

As long as we're together honey I don't care,

'Cause you've started something,

Oh, can't you see?

That ever since we met,

You've had a hold on me,

No matter what you do,

I only want to be with you.

With her outrageous beehive hairstyles and kohl black panda eyes, Dusty Springfield's looks often outshone her music, but there can be no question that she was the finest white female soul singer of her generation. A legendary "difficult" artist, Dusty began her career as one-third of the The Springfields, a folksy trio that included her brother Tom and future producer Mike Hurst who went on to discover Cat Stevens.

# 1963

# If I Ruled The World

Words by Leslie Bricusse
Music by Cyril Ornadel
© Copyright 1963 Delfont Music Limited.
All Rights Reserved. International Copyright Secured.

Composer Cyril Ornadel recalls the story behind the song: "Impresario Bernard Delfont asked Teddy Holmes, the Managing Director of Chappell's Music Publishers, to recommend a composer and lyricist to write the score of a stage musical he was producing. The show would star Harry Secombe, and was to be based on the much-loved novel by Charles Dickens, The Pickwick Papers.

I had just signed an exclusive contract with Chappell's, and so Teddy Holmes recommended me as the composer and then asked Leslie Bricusse if he would like to write the lyrics. Leslie accepted the commission and was very excited by the project, as he and I had already been working on songs together for a year in the hope of finding a project we could collaborate on.

When we'd completed the score, we first played it to Teddy Holmes who was delighted with the numbers – but with one major exception. He insisted that 'If I Ruled The World' should be replaced with a big, ballad-type song (these were popular at the time) so Harry Secombe would have a hit song from the show.

As you might expect, Leslie and I were not willing to cut the song. Thankfully, our producer Bernard Delfont liked it, our director Peter Coe liked it and – most importantly of all – our star Harry Secombe liked it. In fact, he insisted that it stayed in the show. And when Pickwick opened in London, Harry Secombe had a massive hit with 'If I Ruled The World' – indeed it became his signature song for the rest of his long career.

Later on, Leslie Bricusse returned to America, and at a party in New York he met up with Ralph Sharon, the musical director for Tony Bennett, who was choosing material for a new album. Mr. Bennett liked the song so much, he didn't only record it for an album – he also released it as the A-side of a single in the USA. The single gave him a world-wide hit.

Meanwhile, back in England, Teddy Holmes was so furious that the song had stayed in the show that he refused to print the vocal score, even though virtually every West End Musical of the time was published by Chappell's. It was only thirty-five years later that all the songs from Pickwick were finally made available in print!"

Composer/conductor/producer Ornadel also wrote 'Portrait Of My Love' (Matt Monro's first chart hit, produced by George Martin), many TV themes, and several stage musicals including Pickwick, Ann Veronica, Treasure Island and A Kid For Two Farthings.

*Verse 2:*
Please, dear friends, though I may not be the world's physician,
By nature I'm of modest disposition.
Suppose you chose
Instead of men like those, men like these, and these...

*Chorus 2:*
If I ruled the world
Every man would be as free as a bird,
Every voice would be a voice to be heard,
Take my word, we would treasure each day that occured.

If I ruled the world,
**every man would say the world was his friend,**
there'd be happiness that no man could end,
no, my friend, not if I ruled the world.

# 1964 Downtown

Words & Music by Tony Hatch
© Copyright 1964 ATV Music Limited.
Sony/ATV Music Publishing (UK) Limited.
All Rights Reserved. International Copyright Secured.

*Verse 2:*
Don't hang around and let your problems surround you,
There are movie shows down town.
Maybe you know some little places to go to where they never close, down town.
Just listen to the rhythm of the gentle bossa nova.
You'll be dancing with them too before the night is over, happy again.
The lights are much brighter there, you can forget all your troubles,
Forget all your cares, so go down town, where all the lights are bright,
Down town, waiting for you tonight.
Down town, you're gonna be alright now.

'Downtown' marked the start of Tony Hatch's successful musical association with Petula Clark, pictured. Hatch maintains that Clark, pictured here living and recording in Paris in the early sixties, was prepared to make one last record in English to see if she could revive her stalled career in her home country and her native language, but none of the three songs Hatch presented to her sounded right. As a final attempt Hatch sang her a largely lyric-less version of 'Downtown', a song he had been inspired to write while walking down Broadway in New York City. She liked it and, although Hatch only finished writing the lyric half an hour before the recording session, 'Downtown' would make her a star all over again, not just in Britain but in the US too.

Just listen to the rhythm of the gentle bossa nova.

# You'll be dancing with them too

before the night is over.

Nina Simone

# Feeling Good

Words & Music by Leslie Bricusse & Anthony Newley
© Copyright 1964 Concord Music Limited.
All Rights Reserved. International Copyright Secured.

It's a new dawn, it's a new day, it's a new life for me.

# 1964

# Goldfinger

Words by Leslie Bricusse & Anthony Newley
Music by John Barry
© Copyright 1964 Sony/ATV Music Publishing (UK) Limited.
All Rights Reserved. International Copyright Secured.

# Golden words

he will pour in your ear,
but his lies can't disguise what you fear.

Who could be more British than James Bond, 007? And who can belt a Bond number better than Bassey? However, Dame Shirley recalls that when she was first approached to record the main title theme, there was one little problem:

"John Barry told me, it's called 'Goldfinger', this is how the melody goes, but we don't have any lyrics yet. Well, the moment I heard it, of course I said yes! That wonderful big tune – *da DA da*! I'm very glad I trusted John because, of course, the lyrics were marvellous, too."

La Bassey remains the only artist to have recorded more than one Bond theme, with 'Moonraker' (and the bizarrely titled 'Mr. Kiss Kiss Bang Bang') also to her credit. However, lyricist Don Black recalls a major bust-up with producer Harry Saltzman about the words for her other smash-hit Bond song, 'Diamonds Are Forever':

"He hated my lyrics! Said they were too sexy (what, too sexy for a Bond movie? I ask you!) – all that stuff about 'touch it, stroke it, and undress it'... He stormed out and slammed the door. So I thought, okay then, that's the end of that. But fortunately (co-producer) Cubby Broccoli liked the song very much, and it stayed in the movie."

Don Black and John Barry, shaken but not stirred, were doubtless very pleased it did..

Pictured: Sean Connery as James Bond & Honor Blackman as Pussy Galore in *Goldfinger*.

# 1964

# The House Of The Rising Sun

Traditional
Arranged by Alan Price

© Copyright 1964 Keith Prowse Music Publishing Company Limited.
All Rights Reserved. International Copyright Secured.

**Slow beat tempo**

1. There is a house in New Or-leans, they call the Ris-ing Sun, and it's been the ruin of ma-ny\_\_ a poor boy, and God, I know\_\_ I'm one.

2. My moth-er was a tai-lor,_____ she sewed my new blue jeans; my

*(Verse 3 see block lyrics)*

fa-ther was a gam-blin' man down in New\_\_ Or-leans.

**1.**

**2.**

3. The

4. Oh! moth-er, tell your child-ren_____ not to do what I have done; spend your lives\_\_ in sin and\_\_ mis-er-y_____ in the house\_\_ of the Ris-ing Sun.

5. Well,\_\_ I've got one foot on the plat-form,_____ the oth-er foot on the train; I'm

*(Verse 6 see block lyrics)*

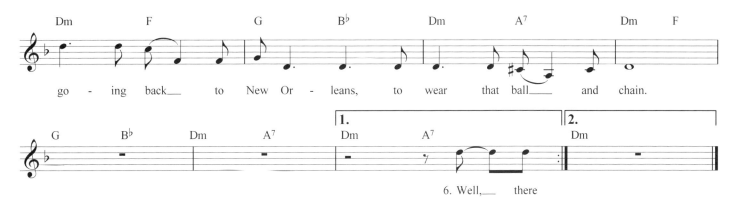

go - ing back___ to New Or - leans, to wear that ball___ and chain.

1. 2.

6. Well,___ there

*Verse 3:*
The only thing a gambler needs
Is a suitcase and a trunk,
And the only time he'll be satisfied
Is when he's all a'drunk.

*Verse 6:*
Well, there is a house in New Orleans
They call the Rising Sun,
And it's been the ruin of many a poor boy,
And God, I know I'm one.

# Oh, mother,
## tell your children not to do what I have done.

Eric Burdon

The oldest known recording of this traditional song dates from 1934 and is by Clarence Ashley and Gwen Foster. It has since been reshaped a number of different artists. American folksinger Dave van Ronk claimed that Bob Dylan had appropriated his arrangement for his for his first Columbia album. However the song – which many believe to have originated in England before it was exported to the US where it acquired a New Orleans setting – found its greatest fame when Newcastle-on-Tyne band The Animals recorded a blistering version in 1964. Eric Burdon's, left, rasping lead vocal gave the song a new urgency and immediately identified it as a definitive blues rock classic for a whole generation.

# She's Not There

Words & Music by Rod Argent
© Copyright 1964 Marquis Music Company Limited.
All Rights Reserved. International Copyright Secured.

**With energy** ♩ = 131

*Verse 2:*
Well no one told me about her, what could I do?
Well no one told me about her, though they all knew.
But it's too late to say you're sorry, how would I know, why should I care?
Please don't bother tryin' to find her, she's not there.
Well let me tell you 'bout the way she looked, the way she acted, the colour of her hair.
Her voice was soft and cool, her eyes were clear and bright, but she's not there.

# 1965

# Catch The Wind

Words & Music by Donovan Leitch
© Copyright 1965 Donovan (Music) Limited.
All Rights Reserved. International Copyright Secured.

**In a relaxed manner**

1. In the chil - ly_____ hours and min - utes_____ of un -
(Verses 2 & 3 see block lyric)

- cer - tain - ty,_____ I want to be_____

in the warm___ hold___ of your lov - ing___ mind.___

___ To feel___

___ you all a - round me_____ and

to take your hand_____ a - long___ the sand.___

Ah, but I may as___ well___ try and catch the wind.___

*To Coda*

La, la,_____ la, la, la la, ya, da, da, da,_____

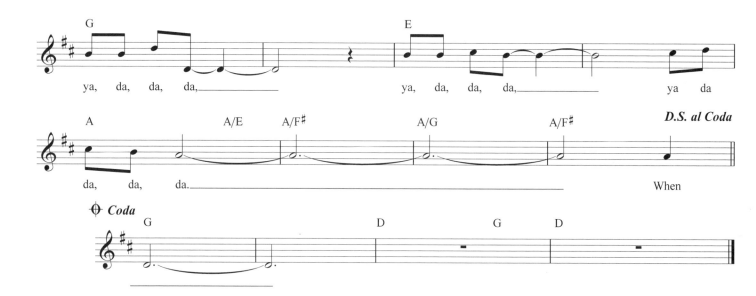

ya,   da,   da,   da,_____      ya,   da,   da,   da,_____      ya   da

da,   da,   da._____      When

**Coda**

*Verse 2:*
When sundown pales the sky,
I want to hide a while behind your smile,
And everywhere I'd look your eyes I'd find.
For me to love you now would be the sweetest thing,
It would make me sing,
Ah, but I may as well try and catch the wind.

*Verse 3:*
When the rain has hung the leaves with tears,
I want you near to kill my fear,
To help me to leave all my blues behind.
For standing in your heart,
Is where I want to be and I long to be,
Ah, but I may as well try and catch the wind.

This pretty song was the first hit single for Donovan Leitch, right, a young Scottish folksinger who was marketed as Britain's answer to Dylan in the mid-sixties. No one ever explained why Dylan needed an answer but, as D.A. Pennebaker's Dylan documentary *Don't Look Back* shows, the pair became friendly on Dylan's 1965 UK tour and, in fact, had rather less in common that was at first thought. If Donovan's self-penned 'Catch The Wind' bears some melodic similarity to Dylan's 'Chimes Of Freedom' their voices are very different, and Donovan would soon go on to become a quite distinctive if rather fey musician in his own right.

# 1965

# Goodbye-ee

Words & Music by Dudley Moore & Peter Cook
© Copyright 1965 TRO Essex Music Limited.
All Rights Reserved. International Copyright Secured.

**Freely**

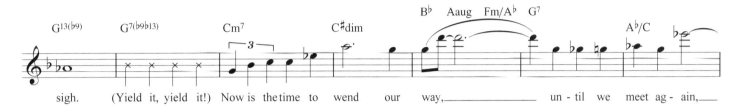

Now is the time to say good-bye. (Good-bye.) Now is the time to yield a

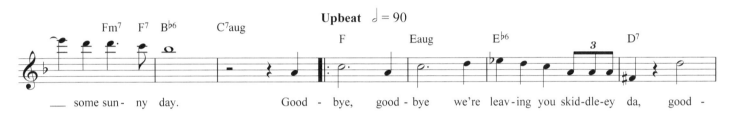

sigh. (Yield it, yield it!) Now is the time to wend our way,_____ un-til we meet ag-ain,_____

**Upbeat** ♩ = 90

_____ some sun - ny day. Good - bye, good - bye we're leav-ing you skid-dle-ey da, good -

- bye,_____ we bid you fond good - bye. Fa - ta ta - ta,_____ fa - ta ta - ta.__ Good - bye, good -

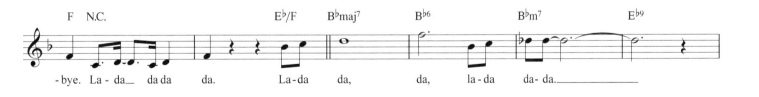

-bye we're leav - ing you skidd-le-ey da, good - bye,_____ we bid you fond good -

-bye. La - da__ da da da. La-da da, da, la-da da-da._____

La - da__ da, da, da. Uh, da, da, da, da, da, da. Good-bye,_____ good - bye we're

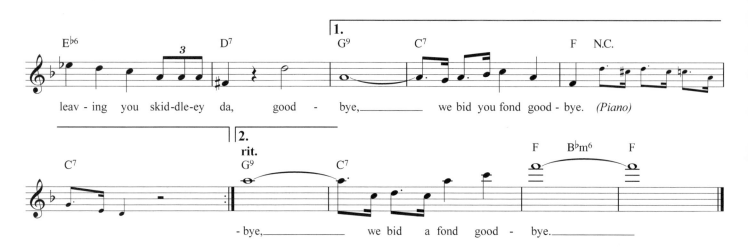

leav - ing you skid-dle-ey da, good - bye,_____ we bid you fond good - bye. *(Piano)*

- bye,_____ we bid a fond good - bye._____

*Spoken over repeated section:*

You know there comes a time in everybody's life when they have to say goodbye. That time is now. So, with tears in either eye, we say goodbye as people have said throughout the years. We leave this mortal coil on which we strut and fret our weary way as Shakespeare put it. God bless him. What a wonderful, odd chap Shakespeare was. Bald but sexy. Oh, take that rhythm away with it's wonderful melodies. Oh, goodbye they say. Goodbye, why not say it again? Goodbye *etc.*

## We leave this
# mortal coil
### on which we strut and fret our
### weary way as Shakespeare put it.

In the good old days, comedians would often finish their act with a song. (Apart from anything else, it was a handy way to get off stage.) So naturally, Dudley Moore, left, and Peter Cook, right, subverted this tradition by ending their TV comedy series, *Not Only... But Also*, with a parody of the genre which also paid homage to the roaring twenties. Indeed, the musical instruction on the manuscript of the song reads: 'Medium Fast – Jazz Feeling – to be sung with a faint aroma of Noël Coward.'

The song is sometimes confused with another song of the same name (featuring the couplet "Good-

bye-ee, good-bye-ee; wipe the tear, baby dear, from your eye-ee") which dates from 1917 and which was memorably revived in *Oh, What A Lovely War.*

Joe McGrath produced the *Not Only... But Also* TV series and remembers:

"Watching Dudley play at rehearsals, Peter would say in a loud voice, 'I wish I'd been forced to play an instrument when I was a child.'

It was well known to everyone concerned with *Not Only... But Also* that Peter's secret wish was to be another, better, Elvis Presley.

The closing song 'Goodbye' gave him his chance.

He couldn't wait to get hold of the microphone on its cable and swing it around. Dudley and his trio feared for their lives.

On some of the shows, Peter's performance of the number reaches an emotional level of intensity that borders on hysteria.

As Dudley plays the opening chord you can hear the audience's gasp of expectation.

Peter's face contorts into an indescribable grimace of joy, before bursting into an uncontrolled, out-of-tune series of interjections aimed to destroy Dudley's perfectly pitched falsetto.

Peter said he enjoyed this

moment most of all.

Watching him, you believe it.

They complement each other perfectly, and his joy is there for all to see."

Dudley composed and performed musical parodies in *Beyond The Fringe*, the stage revue which catapulted Peter Cook, Alan Bennett, Jonathan Miller and Moore himself to enduring fame. He also played jazz with Johnny Dankworth, and scored a number of films, but is perhaps best-remembered for the classic 'Pete and Dud' sketches on TV and for his own starring movies such as *Arthur*.

# 1965

# It's Not Unusual

Words & Music by Gordon Mills & Les Reed
© Copyright 1965 Valley Music Limited.
Universal/MCA Music Limited.
All Rights Reserved. International Copyright Secured.

cra - zy love___ be mine?___

**D.C. al Coda**     ⊕ **Coda**

G⁷     Cmaj⁷     Dm⁷

___     find     that     I'm     in     love___     with     you.___     Woh,___     woh,___

*Fade to end*

Em⁷     Dm⁷     Em⁷     Dm⁷

___     woh,___ woh,___     woh,___ woh,___

Em⁷     Dm⁷     Em⁷     Dm⁷     Cmaj⁷

___     woh,___ woh,___     woh,___ woh.___

*Verse 2:*

It's not unusual to go out at any time,
But when I see you go out and about it's such a crime,
If you should ever want to be loved by anyone,
It's not unusual,
It happens every day, *etc.*

*Verse 3:*

It's not unusual to be mad with anyone,
It's not unusual to be sad with anyone,
But if I ever find you've changed at any time,
It's not unusual to find that I'm in love with you
Woh, woh, *etc.*

**Tom Jones arrived from the Welsh
Valleys with a pony tail and rabbit's
foot talisman dangling from his belt.**

# 1966 | Born Free

Words by Don Black
Music by John Barry

# Bring Me Sunshine

Words by Sylvia Dee
Music by Arthur Kent
© Copyright 1966 Campbell Connelly & Company
Limited (50%)/The International Music Network
Limited (50%).
All Rights Reserved. International Copyright Secured.

**Cheerily** ♩ = 80

Bring me sun-shine___ in___ your smile, bring me laugh-ter___ all___ the while.___ In this world where we live___ ___ there should be more hap-pi-ness,___ so much joy you can give___ to each brand new bright to-mor-row. Make me hap-py through the years,___ nev-er bring me___ an-y tears.___ Let your

On ITV, they were 'Two Of A Kind' (their theme tune during the early 1960s). But when they moved to the BBC in 1968, they became the Sunshine Boys... with this jaunty and joyful signature song. Eric Morecambe and Ernie Wise ruled the comedy ratings – especially at Christmastime – and their partnership has been celebrated again recently in the stage show, *The Play What I Wrote*.

Ernie may have portrayed a budding (if hopeless) playwright in their sketches, but he was also an eager (if frustrated) song-and-dance man. The duo's big musical production numbers were a highlight of each show – their celebrated parody of 'Singin In The Rain' and their wordless choreographed breakfast-making routine to the tune of 'The Stripper' were standouts. Their own musical offerings included several comedy records such as 'Boom - Oo - Ya Ta Ta Ta'.

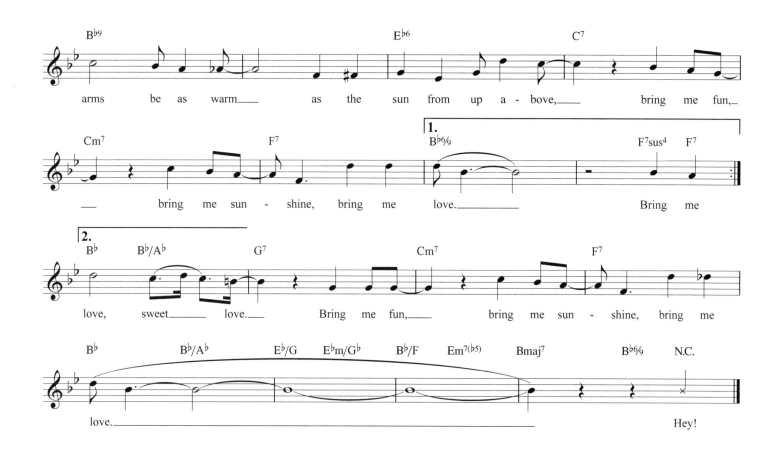

arms be as warm_____ as the sun from up a - bove,_____ bring me fun,

bring me sun - shine, bring me love._____ Bring me

love, sweet_____ love._____ Bring me fun,_____ bring me sun - shine, bring me

love._____ Hey!

Let your arms be as warm
as the sun from up above,
bring me fun,
bring me sunshine,

# bring me love.

# 1966 | Georgy Girl

Words by Jim Dale
Music by Tom Springfield
© Copyright 1966 Springfield Music Limited.
Warner/Chappell Music Limited.
All Rights Reserved. International Copyright Secured.

**Verse 2:**
*(Instrumental)*

Hey there, Georgy girl, dreamin' of the someone you could be.
Life is a reality; you can't always run away.
Don't be so scared of changing and rearranging yourself;
It's time for jumping down from the shelf, a little bit.
Hey there, Georgy girl, there's another Georgy deep inside...

Should five percent appear too small,
# be thankful I don't take it all,
'cause I'm the Taxman,
yeah, I'm the Taxman.

During the Beatle years, George Harrison, above, emerged from the long shadows of Lennon & McCartney as a world-class songsmith in his own right.

'Something' remains his most frequently-covered song, and 'Here Comes The Sun' is possibly his most joyous, while the sardonic 'Taxman' is doubtless here to remind us of the Great British tradition of Supertax. The lyrical asides to Mr. (Harold) Wilson and Mr. (Edward) Heath show an even-handed stance: they were, respectively, Labour and Conservative politicians of the day.

In 1980 Paul Weller based The Jam's Number One song 'Start' on the distinctive guitar and bass riff of this, the edgiest of Harrison's compositions.

# 1966

# Taxman

Words & Music by George Harrison
© Copyright 1966 Northern Songs.
All Rights Reserved. International Copyright Secured.

**Brightly** ♩ = 134

1. Let me___ tell you_ how it___ will be,___ there's one___ for you_ nine-teen___

*(Verses 2, 3 & 4 see block lyrics)*

___ for me,___ 'cause I'm the tax - man, ___

*To Coda* ⊕ *(on repeat)*

yeah,___ I'm the___ tax - man.___

**1.**
2. Should five___
4. Now my___

**2.**

If you drive___ a car,___ I'll tax___ the street,_ if you try___

___ to sit,___ I'll tax___ your_ seat._ If you get___ too cold,_ I'll tax___ the heat,_ if you take___

___ a walk, I'll___ tax___ your_ feet.___ Tax - man.

*(Guitar solo)*

'Cause I'm the tax - man,___

yeah,___ I'm the___ tax - man._____     3. Don't ask___     And you're___

___ work - ing for no - one but___ me.     (Guitar solo)
Tax - man.

*Verse 2:*
Should five percent appear too small,
Be thankful I don't take it all,
'Cause I'm the taxman,
Yeah, I'm the taxman.

*Verse 3:*
Don't ask me what I want it for, (A-ha Mr. Wilson!)
If you don't want to pay some more, (A-ha Mr. Heath!)
'Cause I'm the taxman,
Yeah, I'm the taxman.

*Verse 4:*
Now my advice to those who die,
Declare the pennies on your eyes,
'Cause I'm the taxman,
Yeah, I'm the taxman.

# 1967

# Brown Eyed Girl

Words & Music by Van Morrison
© Copyright 1967 Universal Music Publishing Limited.
All Rights Reserved. International Copyright Secured.

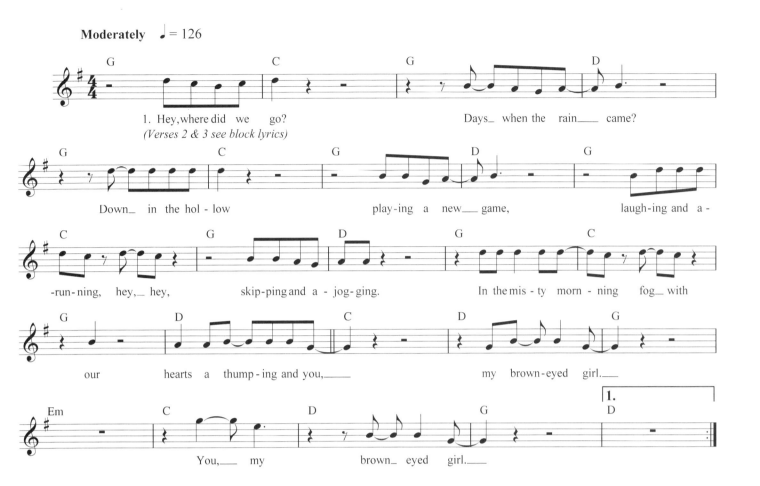

**Moderately** ♩ = 126

1. Hey, where did we go?
*(Verses 2 & 3 see block lyrics)*
Days_ when the rain_ came?

Down_ in the hol - low

play-ing a new_ game,

laugh-ing and a -

-run - ning, hey,_ hey,

skip-ping and a - jog-ging.

In the mis - ty morn - ning fog_ with

our hearts a thump - ing and you,_____

my brown-eyed girl._

**1.**

You,_____ my

brown_ eyed girl._____

Van Morrison began his career fronting Belfast R&B band Them, but soon left them for a long and distinguished career as a singer and songwriter.

**2, 3.**

D
Do you\_ re - mem - ber when     we used to sing,\_ Sha la\_ la la

C          G          D          G
\_ la la\_ la la\_ la la da di da?\_          Sha la\_ la la

C          G          D          G  *D.C. al Fine*
\_ la la\_ la la\_ la la da di da,\_          la di da.\_

*Verse 2:*

Whatever happened to Tuesday and so slow?
Goin' down to the old mine with a transistor radio.
Standing in the sunlight, laughing,
Hide behind a rainbow's wall.
Slipping and a sliding
All along the water fall with you,
My brown-eyed girl.
You, my brown-eyed girl.

*Verse 3:*

So hard to find my way, now that I'm on my own.
Saw you just the other day, my, how you have grown!
Cast my mem'ry back there,
Lord, sometimes I'm overcome thinking about
Making love in the green grass,
Behind the stadium with you,
My brown-eyed girl.
You, my brown-eyed girl.

# Slipping and a sliding all along the waterfall
## with you,
## my brown-eyed girl.

# 1967

# Itchycoo Park

Words & Music by Steve Marriott &
Ronnie Lane
© Copyright 1967 United Artists Music Limited.
EMI United Partnership Limited.
All Rights Reserved. International Copyright Secured.

Brightly ♩ = 90

1. O - ver Bridge of Sighs___ to rest my eyes in shades of green.___
*(Verse 2 see block lyrics)*

Un - der dream - ing spires,___ to It - chy - coo park that's___ where I've been.___ What did you

do there?___ I got high. What did you feel there?___ Well___ I cried. But why the

tears then?___ Tell___ you why.... It's all___ too beau - ti - ful,

it's all___ too beau - ti - ful,___ it's all___ too beau - ti - ful,___

it's all___ too beau - ti - ful.___ I___ feel in - clined to blow___ my mind,___ get hung

up, feed the ducks with a bun. They all come out___ to groove___ a - bout,___ be

nice and have fun in the sun. It's all___ too beau - ti - ful,___

it's all___ too beau - ti - ful,___ it's all___ too beau - ti - ful.___

Hah.

It's all___ too beau - ti - ful.___

*Verse 2:*
I'll tell you what I'll do, (What will you do?)
I'd like to go there now with you.
You can miss out school, (Won't that be cool?)
Why go learn the words of fools?
What will we do there? We'll get high.
What will we touch there? We'll touch the sky.
But why the tears then? I'll tell you why.

I feel inclined to blow my mind, get hung up,
# feed the ducks with a bun.

**Always elegant and dapper, The Small Faces personified the Mod movement in London during the mid-Sixties. Left to right, Ian Mclagan, Kenney Jones, Steve Marriott, Ronnie Lane.**

# 1967

# Love Is All Around

Words & Music by Reg Presley
© Copyright 1967 Dick James Music Limited.
Universal/Dick James Music Limited.
All Rights Reserved. International Copyright Secured.

**Verse 2:**
I see your face before me as I lay on my bed;
I kinda get to thinking of all the things you said
You gave your promise to me, and I gave mine to you;
I need someone beside me, in everything I do.

# 1967 | Nights In White Satin

Words & Music by Justin Hayward
© Copyright 1967 Tyler Music Limited.
All Rights Reserved. International Copyright Secured.

**Ballad** ♩. = 56

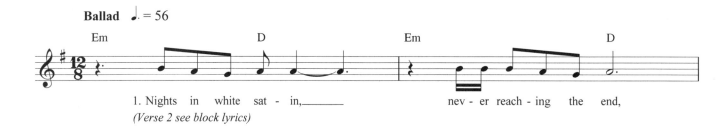

1. Nights in white sat - in,_____ nev - er reach - ing the end,
*(Verse 2 see block lyrics)*

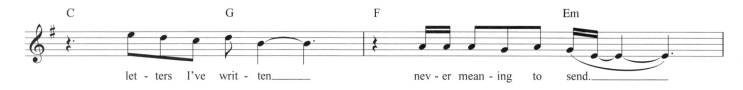

let - ters I've writ - ten_____ nev - er mean - ing to send._____

Beau - ty I'd al - ways missed, with these eyes____ bef - ore,

just what the truth is____ I can't say an - y - more,_____ 'cause I

love you,____ yes, I____ love you.____ Oh, how____ I love____ you._____

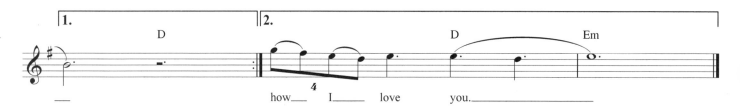

**1.** ____ 

**2.** how____ I____ love you._____

4

*Verse 2:*

Gazing at people, some hand in hand,
Just what I'm going through, they can't understand.
Some try to tell me thoughts they cannot defend,
Just what you want to be, you'll be in the end.
And I love you, yes, I love you.
Oh, how I love you, how I love you.

Some try to tell me thoughts they cannot defend, just what you want to be,

# you'll be in the end.

**The Moody Blues started out as an R&B blues band from Birmingham but changed their style to incorporate concept albums with a softer hybrid of ballads and symphonic rock. Left to right, John Lodge, Graeme Edge, Mike Pinder, Ray Thomas & Justin Hayward**

# 1967

# Puppet On A String

Words & Music by Phil Coulter & Bill Martin
© Copyright 1967 Peter Maurice Music Company Limited.
All Rights Reserved. International Copyright Secured.

With a bounce ♩ = 126

I_____ won-der if one day that you'll say that you care, if you say you love me mad-ly, I'll glad-ly be there, like a pup-pet on a string._____

1. Love is just like a mer-ry-go-round,_ with all the fun of the fair.___ One day I'm feel-ing

*(Verse 2 see block lyrics)*

down on the ground,_ then I'm up in the air.___ Are you lead-ing me on?___ To-mor-row will you be gone?_____ I_____ won-der if one

day that you'll say that you care, if you say you love me mad-ly, I'll glad-ly be there, like a pup-pet on a

string._____ Like a pup-pet on a... string!

*Verse 2:*

I may win on the roundabout, then I'll lose on the swings.

In or out, there is never a doubt just who's pulling the strings.

I'm all tied up in you, but where's it leading me to?

Even by the standards of the sixties, 1967 was an extraordinary year for British pop music. It was the year of *Sgt Pepper*… when The Who, Pink Floyd and The Move played The Roundhouse… the year the Bee Gees arrived on the scene… Bowie's debut album was released… flowers were the power… Steve Winwood left the Spencer Davis Group to create Traffic… Fleetwood Mac appeared at the Windsor Jazz & Blues Festival… and all kinds of music was happening (man!) everywhere. In that self-same year, Petula Clark had a hit with 'This Is My Song' (written by Charlie Chaplin) and Engelbert Humperdinck topped the charts with 'The Last Waltz'.

Bill Martin, co-writer of 'Puppet On A String,' recalls meeting a friend in London's very own Tin Pan Alley, Denmark Street: "I bumped into Denny Cordell (he was a fantastic producer, made 'Go Now'), and he said, 'I've just produced a Number One!' So I replied, 'Well, I've just written a Number One!' In those days, you had to have demonstration records – nobody had i-Pods or Walkmans then. So we went back to my office to play the records. He said, 'You put yours on first,' and I said, 'No, you put yours on first.' Well, he put on 'A Whiter Shade of Pale' and I nearly died. I said, 'That will be Number One all over the world, it's quite fantastic'. Of course, it was based on a Bach tune but the words were so esoteric and so sixties – I just

knew it would be huge. So then he said, 'Now put yours on,' and I played him 'Puppet On A String' (performed by Sandie Shaw, above). He looked at me incredulously and he said, 'Are you going to release that?' I replied, 'Well, yes, we're putting it in the Eurovision Song Contest.' He said 'That's amazing – it's so different, isn't it?' I said, 'I bet it wins the Eurovision!' And of course it did. I'd really wanted to write a circussy kind of song, and I said to [co-writer] Phil Coulter, 'The best song ever in the Eurovision, although it never won, was 'Volare' – so why don't we have a big long note?' and he said, 'What do you mean? We can't do a long note or we'll get sued.' But I said, 'No! They stole it from

'OOOOOOOOklahoma!'

'Puppet On A String' not only won the Eurovision Song Contest (the first time Britain had ever come top), but it became the quintessential Eurovision Song. Martin & Coulter enjoyed further Euro-success with Ireland's first-ever winning entry, 'All Kinds Of Everything' sung by Dana. Although their 1968 song, 'Congratulations', for Cliff Richard came second in the contest, it became a chart-topper in the UK and worldwide. Better yet, it entered the collective unconscious (on a par with 'Happy Birthday') and is performed at many a festive occasion when congratulations are in order. It was even sung by George Harrison on his 1970 album, *All Things Must Pass*.

# Say You Don't Mind

Words & Music by Denny Laine
© Copyright 1967 The Sparta Florida Music Group Limited.
All Rights Reserved. International Copyright Secured.

**With a driving beat** ♩ = 118

1. I re-al-ise__ that I've been, in your eyes,__ some__ kind of fool.
*(Verses 2 & 3 see block lyrics)*

What I do,__ what I did, stu-pid fish,__ I drank the pool.__

I've been do - ing some dy - ing,__ now I'm do - ing some try -

*To Coda* ⊕

- ing,__ so__ say you don't mind,__ you don't mind,__ you'll let me off this time.__

**1.**

**2.**

To you I'm blind,_____ some-thing in - side.

Say you don't__ mind._____

I've been do - ing some dy - ing,__

now I'm do - ing some try - ing,\_ hey!    Say you don't mind,\_ you don't mind\_

\_ you loved me all this time.\_ For this time,\_ for this time,\_ you loved me all this time.\_

To you I'm blind,_____ some-thing in -

- side._____    Say you don't\_ mind._____

\_you'll let me off this time.\_\_\_\_\_    You'll let me off this time.\_\_\_\_\_

*Verse 2:*
I came in to this scene
When my dreams were getting bad.
And who rides with the tide?
And who's glad with what it had?
I've been doing some whining,
Now I'm doing some finding.
So say you don't mind, you don't mind,
You'll let me off this time.

*Verse 3:*
When it gets you so bad
That a door mat sees better times.
That's the time to get back
And think up some better line.
I've been doing some growing,
But I'm scared of you going.
So say you don't mind, you don't mind,
You'll let me off this time.

When it gets you so bad
# that a doormat sees better times.
That's the time to get back.

# 1967

# Sunshine Of Your Love

Words & Music by Jack Bruce,
Pete Brown & Eric Clapton

Very Solidly ♩ = 116

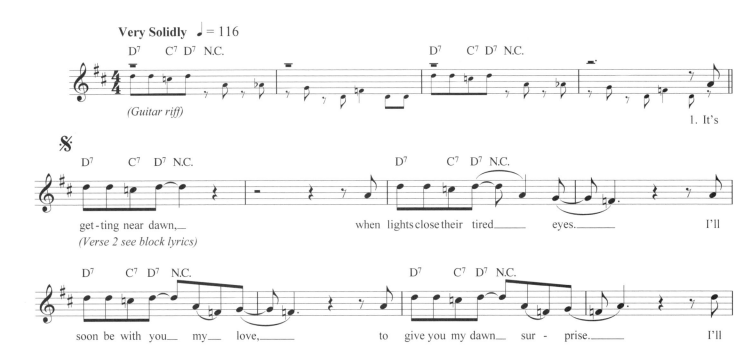

(Guitar riff)

1. It's

get-ting near dawn,— when lights close their tired—— eyes.—— I'll

(Verse 2 see block lyrics)

soon be with you— my— love,——— to give you my dawn— sur - prise.——— I'll

Cream was the first British
supergroup, incorporating the talents
of three musicians who'd already
found fame and success elsewhere.
Left to right, Jack Bruce, Ginger Baker
& Eric Clapton.

*Verse 2:*
I'm with you love;
The light shining through on you,
Yes, I'm with you my love,
It's the morning and just we two,
I'll stay with you, darling, now,
I'll be with you 'til my seeds are dried up.

# Waterloo Sunset

Words & Music by Ray Davies
© Copyright 1967 Davray Music Limited.
Carlin Music Corporation.
All Rights Reserved. International Copyright Secured.

**Lazily** ♩ = 100

1. Dir-ty old riv-er must you keep roll-ing flow-ing in-to the night,

*(Verses 2 & 3 see block lyrics)*

Peo-ple so bu-sy, make me feel diz-zy, ta-xi lights shine so bright.

But I don't need no friends.

*To Coda*

As long as I gaze on Wa-ter-loo sun-set, I am in par-ra-dise.

Ev-'ry day I look at the world from my win-dow.

The chil-ly, chil-li-est eve-ning time. Wat-er-loo sun-set's fine.

*D.S. al Coda (after repeat)*

(Wat-er-loo sun set's fine.) 2. Ter-ry meets Ju-

*Coda*

- set they are in pa-

*guitar solo*

- ra-dise.

Wat-er-loo sun-set's fine. (Wat-er-loo sun-set's fine.)

## Verse 2:

Terry meets Julie, Waterloo Station, every Friday night.
But I'm so lazy, don't want to wander, I stay at home at night.
But I don't feel afraid,
As long as I gaze on Waterloo sunset,
I am in paradise.

## Verse 3:

Millions of people, swarming like flies 'round Waterloo underground.
Terry and Julie cross over the river, where they feel safe and sound.
And they don't need no friends.
As long as they gaze on Waterloo sunset,
They are in paradise.

# But I don't feel afraid,
as long as I gaze on Waterloo sunset
I am in Paradise.

Not just one of Ray Davies' best songs but, in the opinion of many, one of the all-time great British pop songs. A London FM radio poll in 2004 named this the "Greatest Song About London", while *Time Out* named it the "Anthem of London" – ironic, since one of the earliest stories that attached itself to the song was that its original title had been 'Liverpool Sunset'. (Davies, above, claimed at the time that Liverpool had become a sixties cliché so he changed it to Waterloo). Rumours that the song's Terry and Julie referred to swinging sixties icons Terence Stamp and Julie Christie were dismissed by Davies, but in the end all that mattered was that The Kinks' lead man had come up with a haunting and evocative song that many rate among the very best of his wry observational songs.

# 1967

# Whiter Shade Of Pale

Words by Keith Reid
Music by Gary Brooker  +J.S.Bach
© Copyright 1967 Onward Music Limited.
All Rights Reserved. International Copyright Secured.

**Tenderly, at a moderate pace**

1. We skipped the light fan - dan - go,
(Verse 2 see block lyrics)
and turned cart - wheels___ 'cross the

floor.___ I was feel-ing kind of sea-sick, but the crowd called___ out for more,

the room was hum-ming hard - er as the ceil-ing flew a - way.___

When we called out for a - noth - er drink, the wait - er brought a tray.___ And so it

was___ that la - ter as the mil-ler told his tale,___ that her face, at first just

ghost - ly, turned a whi - ter___ shade of pale.___ pale.___

*Verse 2:*

She said "There is no reason,
And the truth is plain to see".
But I wandered through my playing cards,
And would not let her be.
One of sixteen vestal virgins
Who were leaving for the coast,
And altho' my eyes were open,
They might just as well be closed.

And so it was that later
As the miller told his tale,
That her face, at first just ghostly,
Turned a whiter shade of pale.

# 1968

# Black Magic Woman

Words & Music by Peter Green
© Copyright 1968 King Music Publishing Company Limited.
Bourne Music Limited.
All Rights Reserved. International Copyright Secured.

Verse 2:

Don't turn your back on me baby,

Don't turn your back on me baby.

Yes, don't turn your back on me baby; stop messing 'round with your tricks.

Don't turn your back on me baby, you just might pick up my magic sticks.

Verse 3:

You got your spell on me baby,

You got your spell on me baby.

Yes, you got your spell on me baby; turning my heart into stone.

I need you so bad, magic woman, I can't leave you alone.

# 1968

# Eloise

Words & Music by Paul Ryan
© Copyright 1968 Carlin Music Corporation.
All Rights Reserved. International Copyright Secured.

Verse 2:

My Eloise is like the stars that please the night,
The sunlight makes the day that lights the way,
And when that star goes by,
I'll hold it in my hands and cry,
"Love is mine, my love will shine."

Verse 3:

And as the days grow old the nights grow cold,
I want to hold her near to me,
I know she's dear to me,
And only time can tell and take away this lonely hell,
I'm on my knees to Eloise.

# Hey Jude,
you'll do
the movement you need is on your shoulder.

# 1968 | Hey Jude

Words & Music by John Lennon & Paul McCartney
© Copyright 1968 Northern Songs.
All Rights Reserved. International Copyright Secured.

Ballad ♩ = 75

1. Hey Jude, don't make it bad, take a sad song and make it bet - ter. Re-

-mem - ber to let her in to your heart, then you can start, to make it bet - ter. 2. Hey

Jude, don't be a - fraid, you were made to go out and get her. The
*(Verse 3 see block lyric)*

min - ute you let her und - er your skin, then you beg - in to make it bet - ter.

And an - y time you feel the pain, hey Jude, ref - rain don't car - ry the world up - on your shoul-

- der. For well you know that it's a fool who plays it cool by mak - ing his world

a lit - tle cold - er. Na, na, na, na, na, na, na, na, na.

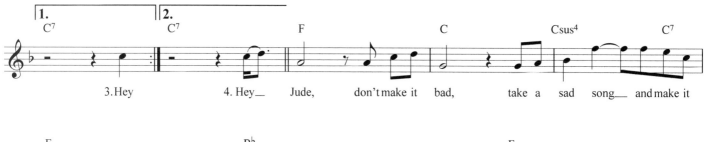

3. Hey    4. Hey___ Jude,    don't make it bad,    take a  sad  song___ and make it

bet - ter.___    Rem – em – ber    to  let her  in___ to your  skin,    then you beg – in,___

___    to  make  it    bet – ter, bet – ter, bet – ter, bet – ter,    bet – ter, bet – ter, ow.

*Repeat ad lib. to fade*

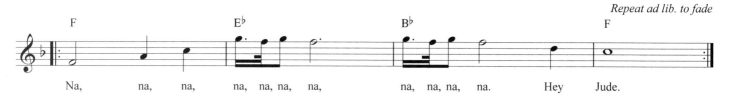

Na,    na,    na,    na, na, na, na,    na, na, na, na.    Hey    Jude.

*Verse 3:*
Hey Jude, don't let me down,
You have found her, now go and get her,
Remember to let her into your heart,
Then you can start,
To make it better.

So let it out and let it in,
Hey Jude, begin,
You're waiting for someone to perform with,
And don't you know that it's just you,
Hey Jude, you'll do,
The movement you need is on your shoulder,
Na, na, na, na, na, na, na, na, na, yeah.

# 1968

# Lily The Pink

Traditional
Arranged by John Gorman, Roger
McGough & Mike McGear

**D.S. al Coda 3**

*Coda 3*
**Rubato**

8. Up to heav-en her soul asc-end-ed for the church bells they did ring.___ She took

with her med-i-cin-al com-pound; hark! The her-ald ang-els sing. *Chorus:* We'll

**a tempo**

drink a drink a drink to Li-ly the pink the pink the pink, the sav-iour

of___ the hum-an race.___ For she in-

**molto rit**

-vent-ed___ med-i-cin-al com-pound,___ most ef-fi-

-ca-cious___ in ev-ery case.___

*Verse 3:*
Old Ebenezer thought he was Julius Caesar,
And so they put him in a home,
Where they gave him medicinal compound,
And now he's Emperor of Rome.

*Verse 5:*
Aunty Millie ran willy-nilly,
When her legs they did recede,
And so they hooked on medicinal compound,
Now they call her Millepede.

*Verse 7:*
Lily the pink she, turned to drink she,
Filled up with paraffin inside,
And despite her medicinal compound,
Sadly Picca-Lily died.

Have you seen the old girl who walks the streets of London, **dirt in her hair** and her clothes in rags?

Ralph McTell's most famous song reflected his busking experiences all over Europe and distilled them into a single city. When the song first appeared in 1969 it was on McTell's album *Spiral Staircase* and it was not released as a single until 1974. 'Streets Of London' then reached number two in the UK singles chart, only later coming to mean different things to different people. A Godsend to London buskers and still a favourite with many nostalgic folk fans, the song has also gained a less welcome reputation as an anthem of sanctimonious hippie concern.

# 1968    Streets Of London

Words & Music by Ralph McTell
© Copyright 1968 Westminster Music Limited.
All Rights Reserved. International Copyright Secured.

**Reflectively**  ♩ = 80

1. Have you seen the old man in the closed down mar - ket,
*(Verses 2,3 & 4 see block lyrics)*
kick - ing up the pap - er with his worn out shoes?
In his eyes you see no pride, and held loose - ly at his side,
yes - ter - day's pap - er, tell - ing yes - ter - day's news.
So how can you tell me you're lone - ly,
and say for you that the sun don't shine?
Let me take you by the hand and lead you through the streets of Lon - don;
Show you some - thing to make you change your mind.

**Verse 2:**
Have you seen the old girl who walks the streets of London,
Dirt in her hair and her clothes in rags?
She's no time for talking; she just keeps right on walking,
Carrying her home in two carrier bags.

**Verse 3:**
In the all night café at a quarter past eleven,
Same old man, sitting there on his own.
Looking at the world over the rim of his tea-cup,
Each tea lasts an hour, then he wanders home alone.

**Verse 4:**
Have you seen the old man outside the seaman's mission,
Memory fading with the medal ribbons that he wears?
In our winter city the rain cries a little pity
For one more forgotten hero and a world that doesn't care.

# Who Do You Think You Are Kidding Mr. Hitler?

Words & Music by Jimmy Perry &
Derek Taverner
© Copyright 1968 Veronica Music Limited.
All Rights Reserved. International Copyright Secured.

# 1969

# The Lemon Song

Words & Music by Jimmy Page, Robert Plant, John Paul Jones, John Bonham & Chester Burnett
© Copyright 1969 Jewel Music Publishing Company Limited.
All Rights Reserved. International Copyright Secured.

**Slow Blues** ♩ = 80

1. I should have quit___ you___ a long_ time a-go.___
*(Verses 2-5 see block lyrics)*

Oh,__ oh,___ yeah,___ yeah.___ A long time a-go.___

I would have been here my chil-dren, down on__ this kill-ing floor.___

*Repeat 4 times*

*Verse 2:*
I should have listened baby to my second mind,
I should have listened baby to my second mind,
Every time I go away and leave you darling,
You send me the blues way down the line.

*Verse 3:*
People tell me baby, to keep you satisfied,
People tell me baby, to keep you satisfied,
Let me tell you baby,
You ain't nothing but a two-bit, no-good wife.

*Verse 4:*
I went to sleep last night; I've worked as hard as I can,
Bring home my money, you take my money; give it to another man
I should have quit you baby, such a long time ago,
I wouldn't be here with all my troubles, down on this killing floor.

*Verse 5:*
Squeeze me baby, 'til the juice runs down my leg,
Squeeze me baby, 'til the juice runs down my leg,
The way you squeeze my lemon,
I'm gonna fall right out of bed.

In 1968 Led Zeppelin held their first rehearsal in an upstairs room in London's Chinatown. It grew out of the ashes of The Yardbirds and proved to be one of those happy confluences of talent that worked straight away. The band's blend of classic Delta blues, mystical British folk and contemporary rock was established on their first album and reprised in their second, *Led Zeppelin II*, which featured 'The Lemon Song'. Full of sexual innuendo, the song borrowed sufficiently from Howlin' Wolf's 'Killing Floor' for the blues singer's name to join those of the group's members in the song's credits… but only after legal action. Led Zeppelin, left to right, John Paul Jones, Jimmy Page, Robert Plant & John Bonham.

# 1969

# Living In The Past

Words & Music by Ian Anderson

*Verse 2:*
Once I used to join in,
Every boy and girl was my friend;
Now there's revolution, but they don't know
What they're fighting.
Let us close our eyes,
Outside their lives go on much faster;
Oh, we won't give in,
Let's go living in the past.

# 1969

# Pinball Wizard

Words & Music by Pete Townshend

4.E - ven at my fav-'rite tab - le, he can beat my best, the

kids all lead him in___ and he just does the rest.___ He's got cra - zy flip-per fin - gers,

nev - er seen him fall, that deaf, dumb___ and blind___ kid, sure plays a mean pin -

- ball.

*Repeat to fade*

*Verse 2:*
He stands like a statue, becomes part of the machine.
Feeling all the bumpers, always playing clean.
He plays by intuition; the digit counters fall.
That deaf, dumb and blind kid sure plays a mean pinball.

*Verse 3:*
Ain't got no distractions, can't hear those buzzers and bells.
Don't see no lights a-flashin', he plays by sense of smell.
Always get a replay and never tilts at all.
That deaf, dumb and blind kid sure plays a mean pinball.

Ain't got no distractions,
can't hear those buzzers and bells.
Don't see no lights a-flashin',
# he plays by sense of smell.

Written by Pete Townshend, right, for The Who's 1969 rock opera *Tommy*, 'Pinball Wizard' was released as a single in 1969, reaching number four in the UK charts. It was remarkable for its famous introduction in which the sounds of a pinball machine are imitated by guitars, and its rhythmic theme that reappears elsewhere in the opera. The song was in fact a late addition, introduced to offset what was seen as excessive spirituality in the story. Townshend's choice of pinball as the game at which deaf, dumb and blind kid Tommy Walker excelled was partly to elicit approval from Nik Cohn who was advising Townshend on the opera prior to recording; Cohn was a pinball fanatic. Later the song became absorbed into Elton John's repertoire after he sang it in Ken Russell's 1975 film version of *Tommy*.

# 1969

# Something In The Air

Words & Music by John Keen
© Copyright 1969 Fabulous Music Limited.
All Rights Reserved. International Copyright Secured.

# Something In The Air

3. Hand out the arms and am - mo, we're go - ing to blast our way through here.

We've got to get__ to - geth - er soon-er or lat - er, be - cause__ the rev - o - lut - ion's here,__

__ and you know it's right.__ And you know that it's right.

We have got to get it to - geth - er, we have got to get it to - geth - er now.__

**Assembled by The Who's Pete Townshend in 1968, Thunderclap Newman featured the talents of Andy 'Thunderclap' Newman, a GPO engineer and pianist, and Speedy Keen, who was Townshend's chauffeur. Left to right, Jack McCulloch, Keen, Newman and Jimmy McCulloch.**

# 1969

# Who Knows Where The Time Goes?

Words & Music by Sandy Denny
© Copyright 1969 Fairwood Music Limited.
All Rights Reserved. International Copyright Secured.

With a lilt ♩ = 73

1. A - cross the eve - ning sky, all the birds are leav -

*(Verses 2 & 3 see block lyrics)*

- ing. Oh, but then you know it was time for them

to go. By the win - ter

fi - re I will still be dream - ing.

I do not count the time,

for who knows where the time goes?

Who knows where the time

goes?

**D.S. al Coda**

3. I

**To Coda**

**Coda**

Who,

who__ knows_____ where_____ the time_____ goes?_____ Who__

_____ knows_____ where___ the time_____

__ goes?_____

*Verse 2:*
Sad deserted shore,
Your fickle friends are leaving,
Oh, but then you know,
It was time for them to go,
But I will still be here,
I have no thought of leaving,
I do not count the time,
For who knows where the time goes?
Who knows where the time goes?

*Verse 3:*
I know I'm not alone,
While my love is near me,
I know that it's so,
Until it's time to go,
All the storms in winter,
And the birds in spring again,
I do not count the time,
For who knows where the time goes?
Who knows where the time goes?

**Folk rock pioneers Fairport Convention enjoyed their greatest success with Sandy Deny as their lead singer. She is photographed with Fairport's violinist Dave SSwarbrick and guitarist Richard Thompson, seen here on accordian. Sandy (centre) with Fairport Convention.**

Words & Music by Elton John &
Bernie Taupin
© Copyright 1969 Dick James Music Limited.
Universal/Dick James Music Limited.
All Rights Reserved. International Copyright Secured.

In 1968, Elton John, right, and his lyricist partner signed on as staff writers for the publisher Dick James. Their first hit single was 'Your Song', with seventeen-year-old Bernie Taupin's, left, lyrics perfectly conveying the gaucheness and sweetness of young love.

Following a sensational Rocket Man series of hits, Elton crystallised the nation's mourning for Princess Diana when he played and sang a new version of 'Candle In The Wind' at Westminster Abbey. More recently, he has moved into writing for film and theatre: with Tim Rice, he provided the songs for Disney's animated movie, *The Lion King*, which won a Best Song Oscar for 'Can You Feel The Love Tonight' and subsequently became an international hit on stage. The two 'Sirs' – Tim and Elton – have also scored a new musical version of *Aida*. Elton wrote the music for the stage version of *Billy Elliot* and (to bring the story neatly back home) he has recently reunited with his original partner Bernie Taupin to score a musical about the vampire Lestat.

Anyway, the thing is,
what I really mean,
# yours are the sweetest eyes
I've ever seen.

*Verse 3:*

I sat on the roof, and kicked off the moss;

Well a few of the verses, they've got me quite cross.

But the sun's been quite kind while I wrote this song,

It's for people like you that keep it turned on.

*Verse 4:*

So excuse me forgetting, but these things I do,

You see I've forgotten if they're green or they're blue.

Anyway, the thing is, what I really mean,

Yours are the sweetest eyes I've ever seen.

# All Right Now

Words & Music by Paul Rodgers & Andy Fraser
© Copyright 1970 Blue Mountain Music Limited.
All Rights Reserved. International Copyright Secured.

**With a driving beat** ♩ = 120

Whoa,_____ ow! 1. There she

stood in the__ street,___ smil - ing from her head__ to her

*(Verse 2 see block lyrics)*

feet. I said - a, "Hey__ now, what is this___ now, ba - by?" May - be, may-

- be she's in need__ of a kiss__ I said - a "Hey,___ uh huh, what's your

name___ ba - by? May - be we can see things__ the same__ Now don't you

wait___ or he - si - tate,___ let's move be - fore they raise_ the park-ing rate."

All right now,___ ba - by it's - a all right___ now.___

All right now,___ ba - by it's - a all right___ now,___ woh.__

Let me tell you now (Mm, eh.) 2. I took her

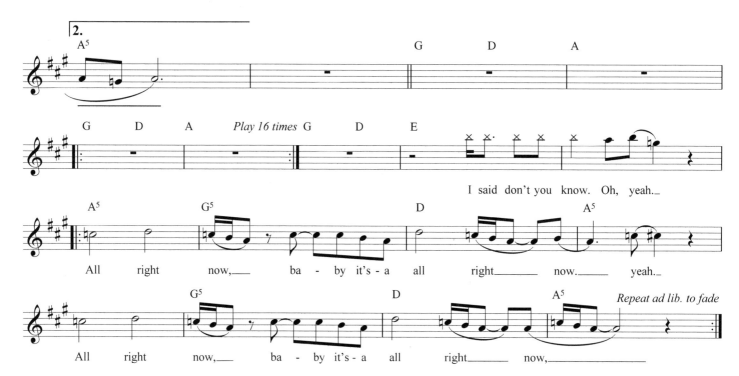

Play 16 times

I said don't you know. Oh, yeah._

All    right    now,___    ba - by it's - a    all    right___    now.____    yeah._

All    right    now,___    ba - by it's - a    all    right___    now,_____

*Repeat ad lib. to fade*

*Verse 2:*
I took her home to my place,
Watching ev'ry move on her face.
She said, "Look, what's your game, baby?
Are you try'n' to put me in shame?"
I said-a "Slow, don't go so fast.
Don't you think that love can last?"
She said "Love, Lord above,
Now you're try'n' to trick me in love."

# 1970

# In The Summertime

Words & Music by Ray Dorset
© Copyright 1970 Broadley Music International
Limited/Associated Music Int
Universal Music Publishing Li
Music Publishing (UK) Limited
All Rights Reserved. International Copyright Secured.

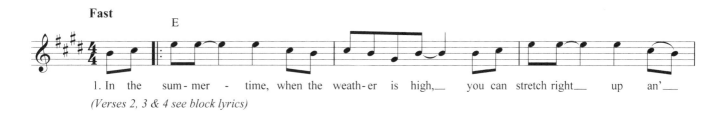

**Fast**

1. In the sum-mer - time, when the weath-er is high,___ you can stretch right___ up an'___

*(Verses 2, 3 & 4 see block lyrics)*

touch___ the sky;___ when the weath-er's___ fine, you got wom-en you got wom-en on your mind.

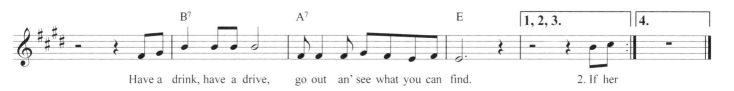

Have a drink, have a drive, go out an' see what you can find. 2. If her

| 1, 2, 3. | 4. |

**Verse 2:**

If her daddy's rich take her out for a meal,
If her daddy's poor just do as you feel.
Speed along the lane, do a ton, or a ton an' twenty-five.
When the sun goes down you can make it, make it good in a lay-by.

**Verse 3:**

We're not grey people, we're not dirty, we're not mean;
We love everybody but we do as we please.
When the weather's fine we go fishing, or go swimming in the sea.
We're always happy, life's for living, yeah! That's our philosophy.

**Verse 4:**

When the winter's here, yeah! It's party time;
Bring a bottle, wear your bright clothes, it'll soon be summertime.
And we'll sing again, we'll go driving or maybe we'll settle down.
If she's rich, if she's nice, bring your friends an' we'll all go into town.

The Good Earth was an obscure skiffle/jug band when their singer/songwriter/guitarist Ray Dorset, left, wrote 'In The Summertime'. Rechristening themselves after Mungojerrie in T.S. Eliot's *Old Possum's Book Of Practical Cats*, the group enjoyed a huge hit with the song after playing it at a 1970 music festival near Newcastle-under-Lyme. They went on to record several more Dorset compositions that reflected his love of skiffle, blues and early rock 'n' roll, but 'In The Summertime', with its incisive rhythm and infectious melody was the summer anthem that became one of the highest selling recordings of all time with an estimated 23 million copies sold. Ten years later Dorset wrote a song with Elvis in mind – 'Feels Like I'm In Love' – which he ultimately produced for Kelly Marie, scoring a substantial disco hit.

# 1970

# Lucky Man

Words & Music by Greg Lake
© Copyright 1970 Leadchoice Limited.
All Rights Reserved. International Copyright Secured.

**Slowly** ♩. = 54

1. He____ had white hors - es, and lad - ies____ by the score.
*(Verses 2, 3 & 4 see block lyrics)*

All____ dressed in sat - in, and wait - ing____ by the door.____

Ooh,____ what a luck - y man____ he was.____

Ooh,____ what a luck - y man____ he was.____

*Repeat 3 times*

*Verse 2:*
White lace and feathers, they made up his bed.
A gold covered mattress, on which he was led.

*Verse 3:*
He went to fight wars, for his country and his king.
Of his honour and his glory, the people would sing.

*Verse 4:*
A bullet had found him, his blood ran as he cried;
Nobody could save him, so he laid down and he died.

# All dressed in satin,
### and waiting by the door.
## Ooh, what a lucky man he was.

# 1970 | Northern Sky

Words & Music by Nick Drake
© Copyright 1970 Warlock Music Limited.
All Rights Reserved. International Copyright Secured.

Moderately ♩ = 94

1, 4. I nev-er felt mag - ic cra - zy as this, I nev-er saw moons, knew the
*(Verses 2 & 3 see block lyrics)*
mean-ing of the sea. I nev-er held em-o-tion in the palm of my hand,
or felt sweet breez-es in the top of a tree.__ But now you're here, bright-en my north-ern sky.__

*Verse 2:*
I've been a long time that I'm waiting,
Been a long time that I've blown.
I've been a long time that I've wandered,
Through the people I have known.
Oh, if you would and you could,
Straighten my new mind's eye.

*Verse 3:*
Would you love me for my money?
Would you love me for my head?
Would you love me through the winter?
Would you love me till I'm dead?
Oh, if you would and you could,
Come and blow your horn on high.

I never held emotion in the palm on my hand,
or felt sweet breezes in the top of a tree.

# But now you're here,
brighten my northern sky.

Black Sabbath's 'Paranoid' reached number four in the UK charts in 1970, quite a feat for a heavy metal band. Singer Osbourne is pictured here in the studio.

# 1970

# Paranoid

Words & Music by Ozzy Osbourne,
Tony Iommi, Terry 'Geezer' Butler
& Bill Ward
© Copyright 1970 Westminster Music Limited.
All Rights Reserved. International Copyright Secured.

**With a driving beat** ♩ = 165

1. Fin-ished with_ my wo-man 'cos_ she could-n't help_ me with my mind,
*(Verses 2 & 3 see block lyrics)*

peo-ple think_ I'm in-sane be-cause_ I_ am frown-ing all the time.

Can you help_ me

oc - cu - py_ my brain?_____ Oh_____

yeah._

*D.C. al Coda*
*(after repeat)*

Coda

4. Make a joke_ and I____ will sigh_ and you_
*(Verse 5 see block lyrics)*

__ will laugh_ and I____ will cry, hap-pi-ness__ I can-not feel and_ love

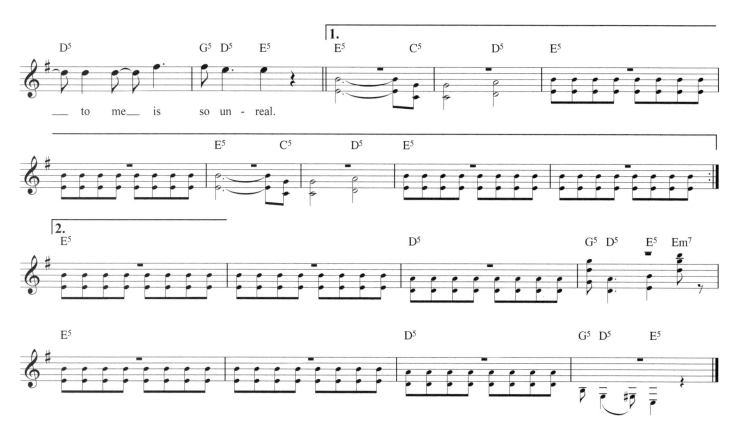

_____ to me___ is   so   un - real.

*Verse 2:*
All day long I think of things,
But nothing seems to satisfy.
Think I'll lose my mind,
If I don't find something to pacify.

*Verse 3:*
I need someone to show me the things
In life that I can't find.
I can't see the things that
Make true happiness, I must be blind.

*Verse 5:*
And so as you hear these words,
Telling you now of my state.
I tell you to enjoy life,
I wish I could, but it's too late.

I tell you to enjoy life,
I wish I could, but it's too late.

# 1970 Wild World

Words & Music by Cat Stevens

Moderately ♩ = 76

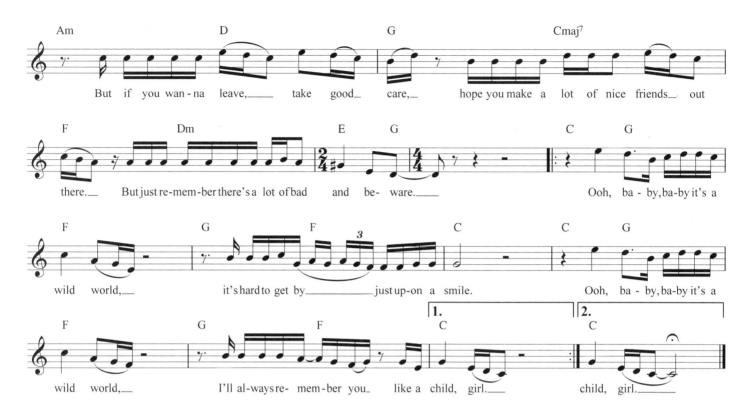

But if you wan-na leave,___ take good___ care,___ hope you make a lot of nice friends___ out

there.___ But just re-mem-ber there's a lot of bad and be-ware.___ Ooh, ba-by, ba-by it's a

wild world,___ it's hard to get by___ just up-on a smile. Ooh, ba-by, ba-by it's a

wild world,___ I'll al-ways re-mem-ber you_ like a child, girl.___ child, girl.___

*Verse 2:*

You know I've seen a lot of what the world can do,

And it's breaking my heart in two, because I never want to see you sad girl.

Don't be a bad girl,

But if you want to leave, take good care,

Hope you make a lot of nice friends out there,

But just remember there's a lot of bad and beware.

Before he was Yusuf Islam but after he was Stephen Demetre Georgiou, the composer of 'Wild World' was Cat Stevens, left, a man who sold 40 million records during the sixties and seventies. 'Wild World' was the most successful single from his *Tea For The Tillerman* album and it was a self-penned goodbye song that incorporated a gloomy prediction: "Oh, baby, baby, it's a wild world / It's hard to get by just upon a smile". In concert Stevens liked to say that the sentiment was a perpetual one, even if the song itself might not last. It lasted well enough, with cover versions by many artists over the years, including a 2006 reggae version by Jimmy Cliff.

# 1971

# I Did What I Did For Maria

Words & Music by Peter Callander & Mitch Murray

bod - y must die     for the   death  of  my  wife,     yes   I    did  what  I   did___  for  Ma - ri -

- a,___    yes   I    did  what  I   did___  for  Ma - ri  -   a.___   Take  an

*Repeat to fade*

*Verse 2:*
Laughter echoed across from the end of the street,
There was the man I was burning to meet,
And my mind was so calm and so clear,
As I took my revenge for Maria.
And he fell to the ground raising dust all around,
But I knew he was dead long before he went down,
It was quick, it was clean; made it easy on him,
Which is more than he did for Maria,
When he did what he did to Maria.

One of two seventies hits for Tony Christie, left, this is the one that did not get a second lease of life. The other – Christie's recording of '(Is This The Way To) Amarillo' – received an unlikely boost in 2002 when comedian Peter Kay used it in the TV series *Phoenix Nights* and so started a revival of Christie's career. In contrast Peter Callander and Mitch Murray's 'I Did What I Did For Maria' is a dramatic Latin-flavoured revenge song with a dash of mariachi and a sideways glance at Tom Jones' 1968 hit 'Delilah'.

Take an eye for an eye,
and a life for a life,
and somebody must die for the death of my wife.

# 1971

# Imagine

Words & Music by John Lennon
© Copyright 1971 Lenono Music.
All Rights Reserved. International Copyright Secured.

**Moderately**

1. I-mag-ine there's no heav - en; it's ea-sy if you try.

No hell__ be-low__ us, a-bove us on-ly sky.__

I-mag-ine all the peo - ple liv-ing for to-day.__ Ah.__

2. I-mag-ine there's__ no coun - tries, it is-n't hard__ to do.__
*(Verse 3 see block lyrics)*

Noth-ing to kill or die__ for, and no re-lig-ion too.__

I-mag-ine all the peo - ple liv-ing life in peace.__ You,__

you may say__ I'm a dream-er, but I'm not the on-ly one.__

I hope some day__ you'll join__ us,

**1.** and the world__ will be as one.__

**2.** live as one.__

*Verse 3:*

Imagine no possessions, I wonder if you can.
No need for greed or hunger; a brotherhood of man.
Imagine all the people sharing all the world.
You may say I'm a dreamer, but I'm not the only one.
I hope some day you will join us, and the world will live as one.

# You may say I'm a dreamer,

but I'm not the only one.

The seductive title song of John Lennon's 1971 solo album has come to symbolise his particular brand of utopian spiritualism. In fact, he borrowed the basic concept ("Imagine there's no countries/ It isn't hard to do/Nothing to kill or die for/No religion too") from Yoko Ono, who had already used it several times in her writings. Lennon, left, himself described 'Imagine' as "an anti-religious, anti-nationalistic, anti-conventional, anti-capitalistic song" that was accepted because it was "sugar-coated". Not everyone did accept it though, including Neil Innes, ex-Bonzo Dog and Rutles member, whose parody 'How Sweet To Be An Idiot' satisfyingly skewers both the sentiment and the melody.

# 1971

# It Must Be Love

Words & Music by Labi Siffre
© Copyright 1971 MAM (Music Publishing) Limited/
Groovy Music Limited.
Chrysalis Songs Limited.
All Rights Reserved. International Copyright Secured.

**With a steady beat** ♩ = 146

1. I nev - er thought___ I'd miss you half as much___ as I do.___
*(Verse 2 see block lyrics, straight quavers)*

And I nev - er thought___

___ I'd feel___ this way,___ the way I feel___ a - bout you.

**Straight ♪s**

Soon as I wake___ up ev - 'ry night,___ ev - 'ry

day, I know that it's you I need___ to take the blues___ a - way.

It must be love,___ love, love. It must be love,___ love,

love. Noth - ing more,___ noth - ing less:___ love is the best.___

**D.S. al Coda**

**Coda**

*Repeat to fade*

It must be love,___ love, love.

*Verse 2:*
How can it be that we can say so much without words?
Bless you and bless me, bless the bees and the birds.
I've got to be near you every night, every day,
I couldn't be happy any other way.

# 1971
# Maggie May

Words & Music by Rod Stewart & Martin Quittenton

© Copyright 1971 EMI Music Publishing (WP) Limited (50%)/EMI Music Publishing Limited (37.5%)/Warner/Chappell Music Limited (12.5%).
All Rights Reserved. International Copyright Secured.

**Brightly** ♩ = 128

1. Wake up Mag-gie I think I've got some-thing to say to you._ It's
*(Verses 2 & 3 see block lyrics)*

late Sep - tem-ber and I real - ly should be back__ at__ school. I

know I keep you a-mused__ but I feel I'm be - ing used.__ Oh,

Mag-gie I could-n't have tried__ an - y more._____ You

led me a-way from home just to save you from be - ing a - lone. You

stole my heart__ and that's__ what real - ly hurts.__ 2. The

**1, 2.**

**3.**

I sup-pose__ I could col-lect my books_ and get on back to school__

or steal my dad-dy's cue__ and make a liv-ing out of play - ing pool._

Or find my-self a rock 'n' roll band that needs__ a help - ing hand.__

Oh, Mag-gie I wish I'd nev-er seen your face._____

You made a first class fool out of me but I'm as blind as a fool can be

___ You stole my heart_ but I love you an - y- way.___

*Verse 2:*

The morning sun, when it's in your face
Really shows your age.
But that don't worry me none,
In my eyes you're everything.
I laugh at all of your jokes,
My love you didn't need to coax.

Oh, Maggie I couldn't have tried any more.
You led me away from home
Just to save you from being alone.
You stole my soul
And that's a pain I can do without.

*Verse 3:*

All I needed was a friend to lend a guiding hand.
But you turned into a lover
And mother what a lover,
You wore me out.
All you did was wreck my bed,
And in the morning, kick me in the head.

Oh, Maggie I couldn't have tried any more.
You led me away from home
Just to save you from being alone.
You stole my heart
I couldn't leave you if I tried.

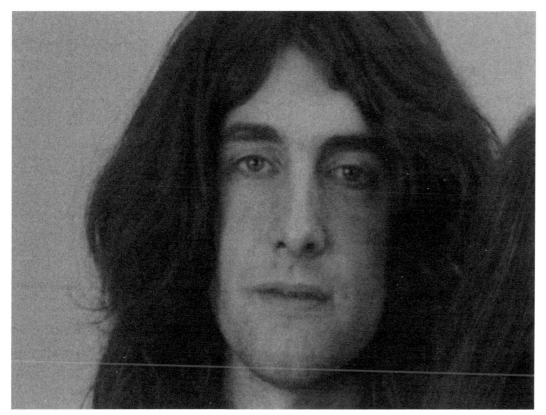

Rod Stewart's signature song shares a title with several traditional melodies, but his version, co-written with Martin Quittenton and recorded with The Faces in 1971, is an original. An allegedly autobiographical song about being seduced by an older woman, it was initially released in Britain as the B-side of the single 'Reason To Believe' but 'Maggie May' received more plays and it soon became the A-side. Its success launched Stewart as a solo artist. A surviving *Top Of The Pops* tape shows Rod and The Faces joined onstage by John Peel, whose pretence at playing the mandolin was inept enough to suggest that he wanted to make it quite clear that this was not a serious attempt to deceive.

# 1972 | All The Young Dudes

Words & Music by David Bowie
© Copyright 1972 Tintoretto Music/RZO Music Limited
(37.5%)/EMI Music Publishing Limited (37.5%)/
Chrysalis Music Limited (25%).
All Rights Reserved. International Copyright Secured.

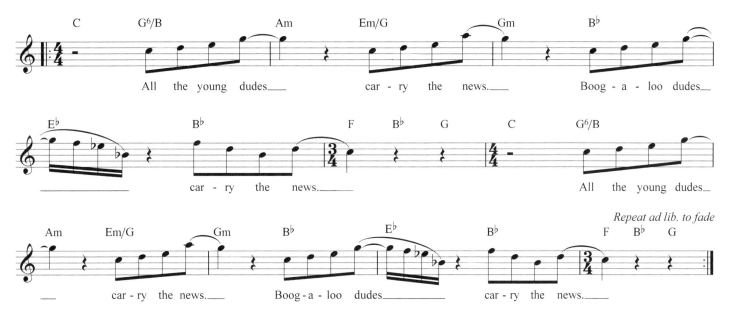

All the young dudes___ car - ry the news.___ Boog - a - loo dudes___

car - ry the news.___ All the young dudes___

*Repeat ad lib. to fade*

__ car - ry the news.___ Boog - a - loo dudes___ car - ry the news.___

*Verse 2:*

Now Jimmy's looking sweet though he dresses like a queen

He can kick like a mule, it's a real mean team,

We can love, oh, we can love,

And my brother's back home with his Beatles and his Stones,

We never got off on that revolution stuff,

What a drag; too many snags,

Well I drunk a lot of wine and I'm feeling fine,

Gonna race some cat to bed,

Is this concrete all around or is it in my head?

Oh brother you guessed.

I'm a dude.

# Well I drunk a lot of wine and I'm feeling fine,
## gonna race some cat to bed.
# Is this concrete all around or is it in my head?

Released in July 1972, 'All The Young Dudes' reached number three in the UK charts. Previously Mott The Hoople had been struggling and was on the point of disbandment when this gift of a song from David Bowie (allegedly witten in haste on the floor of a London flat in the company of the Mott's lead singer, Ian Hunter) turned around the band's fortunes. Despite its downbeat themes of drug abuse, depression, shoplifting and suicide 'All The Young Dudes' would become something of an anthem for the glam-rock movement, and in 1973 Bowie would perform the song on his own tour.

# 1972     Clair

Words & Music by Gilbert O'Sullivan
© Copyright 1972 Sony/ATV Music Publishing (UK) Limited.
All Rights Reserved. International Copyright Secured.

*Verse 2:*
Clair, if ever a moment so rare
Was captured for all to compare,
That moment is you;
It's all that you do.

But why, in spite of our age difference, do I cry?
Each time I leave you I feel I could die;
Nothing means more to me than hearing you say,
"I'm going to marry you,
Will you marry me, Uncle Ray?"
Oh, Clair, Clair.

But try as hard as I might do,
I don't know why you get to me in a way I can't describe.
Words mean so little when you look up and smile,
I don't care what people say,
to me you're more than a child, oh Clair.

# 1972

# In A Broken Dream

Words & Music by David Bentley
© Copyright 1972 Minder Music Limited.
All Rights Reserved. International Copyright Secured.

**With energy** ♩ = 86

1. Ev -'ry day_ I spend my time drink- in' wine, feel- in' fine, wait- in' here_ to find the sign_

*(Verse 2 see block lyrics)*

that I_____ can un- der- stand,_ yes I am._ In the days_ be- tween the

hours, iv -'ry tow- ers, blood- y flow'rs push their heads in- to the air, I don't care if_ I

ev- er know,_ there I go._ Don't push your luck_ too

far, your wounds won't leave_ a scar, right now is where_ you

are in a bro- ken dream._ Did some- one bow their head,

___ did some- one break_ the bread? Good peo- ple are_ in

1.

bed be- fore nine o'- clock._ 2. On the pad_ be- fore my

bro - ken dream,___          and  don't  you  for - get     what  I     said._____

Gm/F                    Em⁷⁽♭⁵⁾                    E♭maj⁷                    *Repeat to fade*

*Verse 2:*
On the pad before my eyes,
Paper cries,
Tellin' lies,
The promises you gave
From the grave of a broken heart,
Ev'ry day I spend my time drinkin ' wine,
Feelin' fine waitin' here to find a sign
That I can understand.
*(Instrumental)*
Don't push your luck too far,
Your wounds won't leave a scar,
Right now is where you are in a broken dream.
Don't push your luck too far,
You know your wounds won't even leave a scar,
Right now is where you are, in a broken dream.

**Python Lee Jackson was the
name of an Australian group
based in London who in 1969
were cuttin demos when
the producer suggested that
the then little known Rod
Stewart might sing on this
particular track. When Rod
became famous as the lead
singer with The Faces, it
was reissued and became a
number three hit in 1972.**

# Living Next Door To Alice

Words & Music by Nicky Chinn & Mike Chapman

© Copyright 1972 Chinnichap Publishing Limited.
BMG Music Publishing Limited.
All Rights Reserved. International Copyright Secured.

**Country feel**  ♩ = 120

1. Sal - ly called_ when she got the word,_ and she said I s'pose you've heard,
*(Verse 2 see block lyrics)*

'bout Al - ice. Well I

rushed to the wind-ow and I looked out - side,_ and I could hard - ly bel - ieve my eyes,_

as the big lim-ous-ine rolled up in - to Al-ice-'s drive._ Oh, I

don't know why she's leav - ing or where she's gon - na go,_ I guess she's got her reas - ons but I

just don't want to know, 'cause for twen-ty four years I've been liv-ing next door to Al-ice.

Twen - ty four years just wait - ing for a chance,_ to tell her how I feel and may - be

get a sec-ond glance, no I'll nev-er get used to not liv-ing next door to Al-ice.

Written and performed by Smokie, this was the biggest hit the group ever had. In a career marked by many false starts and mis-steps, the band that was originally formed in Bradford, Yorkshire, in 1965 enjoyed a run of catchy hits in the mid-seventies but looked set for slow decline until this song made an unexpected comeback in 1995. The band decided to capitalise on audiences' irreverent tendency to shout out "Who the f--- is Alice?" during their performance of the song, so they re-recorded a version that had comedian Roy 'Chubby' Brown shouting out the phrase. It reached the UK Top Ten .
Writer and composer, Nicky Chinn, left, and Mike Chapman.

3. Sal - ly called back    and asked how I felt,__    and she said    I know how to help,__

get ov - er Al - ice,    She said now

Al - ice is gone,__    but I'm still here,__    you know I've been wait - ing    twen - ty four years,__

*freely*  N.C.

and the big lim - ous - ine dis - ap - peared.    Oh,    I    don't know why she's leav - ing    or

where she's gonn - a go,___    I    guess she's got her reas - ons but I    just don't want to know, 'cause for

twen - ty four years I've been liv - ing next door    to    Al - ice.

Twen - ty four years just wait - ing for a chance,__    to tell her how I feel and may - be

get a sec - ond glance, no I'll nev - er get used to not    liv - ing next door to Al - ice.

**Slower**

No I'll nev - er get used to not    liv - ing next door    to    Al - ice.

*Verse 2:*
We grew up together,
Two kids in the park;
Carved our initials deep in the bark,
Me and Alice.
Now she walks through the door with her head held high,
And just for a moment I caught her eye,
As the big limousine pulled out of Alice's drive.

# 1972

# May You Never

Words & Music by John Martyn
© Copyright 1972 Warlock Music Limited.
All Rights Reserved. International Copyright Secured.

E(add 9)　　　　A(add 9)/C♯　　　　B　Bsus4　B7　　　E　A/E　E　A/E　B　　1, 2, 3.　　4.　　E　A/E　E

_ and may_ you_ nev - er lose your wo - man ov - er night._____ May you _

*Verse 2:*
May you never lay your head down, without a hand to hold,
May you never make your bed out in the cold.

*Chorus:*
You're just like a good, close sister to me,
And you know that I love you true,
You hold no blade to stab me in my back,
And I know that there's some that do,
Please won't you, please won't you bear it in mind?
Love is a lesson to learn in our time,
Please won't you, please won't you bear it in mind?
For me.

*Verse 5:*
May you never lay your head down without a hand to hold,
May you never make your bed out in the cold.

*Verse 7:*
May you never lose your woman overnight,
May you never lose your woman overnight.

*Verse 3:*
May you never lay your head down , without a hand to hold,
May you never make your bed out in the cold.

*Chorus:*
You're just like a great strong brother of mine,
And you know that I love you true,
You never talk dirty behind my back,
And I know that there's those that do,
Please won't you, please won't you bear it in mind?
Love is a lesson to learn in our time,
Please won't you, please won't you bear it in mind?
For me.

*Verse 6:*
May you never lose your temper if you get hit in a bar room fight,
And may you never lose your woman overnight.

# May you never lose your temper if you get hit in a bar room fight, and may you never lose your woman overnight. May you never lay your head down without a hand to hold,

# may you never make your bed out in the cold.

This wondrous benediction by John Martyn, right, is probably the best-known song by the Scots iconoclast, although his gentle – and sadly unheeded – warning to his friend Nick Drake ("You've been walking the line/You've been living on solid air") is also fondly remembered. 'May You Never' has been covered by Eric Clapton and Iain Archer among others, but Martyn has never quite broken through to the level of commercial success you'd expect for a major talent like his. Displeased with the workings of the industry, he self-produced an album, *Live At Leeds*, which was only available (and this was in pre-internet days) to buyers ordering it by post direct from his home. But *Big Muff* is held in high esteem by fellow-musicians and by his devoted following. He also has an enduring place in pop music history, as his song 'Angeline' was the first CD single ever to be commercially released.

# 1972

# Stuck In The Middle With You

Words & Music by Gerry Rafferty &
Joe Egan

1. Well, I don't___ know why I came here to-night,___ I got the feel-ing that some-thing ain't right.
*(Verse 2 see block lyrics)*

___ I'm so scared___ in case I fall off my chair,___ and I'm wond-'ring how I'll get down the stairs.

___ Clowns___ to the left___ of me, jok-ers to the right,___ here I am,

___ stuck in the mid-dle with you.___ 2. Yes, I'm___ ___ Well, you start-ted out with noth-ing and you're

proud that you're a self-made man. And your friends they all come crawl-ing, slap-

___ you on your back and say "Please,___

please."___ 3. Well, I'm try-ing to make some sense of it all,___
*(Verse 4 see block lyrics)*

___ but I can see___ it makes no___ sense at all.___ Is it___ cool___

___ to go to sleep on the floor? 'Cause I don't think___ that I can take an-y-more.___

G⁷          B♭          F

Clowns___ to the left___ of me, jok - ers to the right.___ Here I am,___

*To Coda* ⊕          *D.S. al Coda*          ⊕ *Coda*

C

___ stuck in the mid - dle with you.___          Well, you          ___          Yes, I'm___

stuck in the mid - dle with you.___          Stuck in the mid - dle with you.___

*Verse 2:*

Yes, I'm stuck in the middle with you,
And I'm wond'ring what it is I should do.
It's so hard to keep the smile from my face,
Losing control, yeah, I'm all over the place.

*Verse 4:*

Well, I don't know why I came here tonight,
I got the feeling that something ain't right.
I'm so scared in case I fall off my chair,
And I'm wond'ring how I'll get down the stairs.

**A hit in 1973, 'Stuck In the Middle With You' by Stealers Wheel became famous as part of the soundtrack of the 1992 Quentin Tarantino movie Reservoir Dogs. Its writers were group members Gerry Rafferty (left) and Joe Egan.**

# 1972    Virginia Plain

Words & Music by Bryan Ferry
© Copyright 1972 EG Music Limited/BMG Songs Limited.
All Rights Reserved. International Copyright Secured.

**Moderately**

1. Make me a deal___ and make it straight,___ all signed and sealed,___ I'll take it.
*(Verses 3 & 5 see block lyrics)*

To Rob-ert E. Lee___ I'll show_ it, I hope and pray___ he don't blow it,'cause

we've been a- round___ a long_ time, just try - try - try___ try tryin' to make make the big__ time....

2. Take me on a rol - ler coas - ter, take me for an air-plane ride.__
*(Verse 4 see block lyrics)*

Take me for a six day won-der,_ but don't you, don't you throw my pride a-side,_ be-sides, what's real and

make_ be - lieve._ Ba - by Jane's in A - ca-pul-co, we're all fly-ing down to Ri - o___ 3. Throw me a line___

got to reach for some-thing new.

*Half spoken:* What's her name, Vir-gin-i - a Plain.

Verse 3:
Throw me a line I'm sinking fast, clutching at straws can't make it.
Havana sound we're trying, hard edge the hipster jiving.
Last picture shows down the drive-in, you're so sheer you're so chic,
Teenage rebel of the week.

Verse 4:
Flavours of the mountain streamline, midnight blue casino floors.
Dance the cha-cha through till sunrise, opens up exclusive doors, oh wow!
Just like flamingoes look the same so, me and you, just we two,
Got to reach for something new.

Verse 5:
Far beyond the pale horizon, some place near the desert strand.
Where my Studebaker takes me, that's where I'll make my stand but wait,
Can't you see that Holzermane, what's her name,
Virginia Plain.

Roxy Music exploded onto the London glam scene in 1972 looking as if they'd arrived from outer space. The early line up featured, let to right, Bryan Ferry, Phil Manzanera, Andy McKay, Paul Thomson, Brian Eno and Graham Simpson.

Flavours of the mountain streamline, midnight blue casino floors.
# Dance the cha-cha through till sunrise,
opens up exclusive doors.

# 1972

# Ziggy Stardust

Words & Music by David Bowie
© Copyright 1972 Tintoretto Music/RZO Music Limited
(37.5%)/EMI Music Publishing Limited (37.5%)/
Chrysalis Music Limited (25%).
All Rights Reserved. International Copyright Secured.

Ooh._____                    Zig - gy played gui - tar._____

*Verse 3:*
Ziggy played for time,
Jiving us that we were Voodoo.
The Kids were just crass;
He was the nazz,
With God-given ass.
He took it all too far,
But boy, could he play guitar.

Making love with his ego,
Ziggy sucked up into his mind.
Like a leper Messiah,
When the kids had killed the man,
I had to break up the band.

Oh yeah. Ooh. Ziggy played guitar.

David Bowie, left with Mick Ronson on *Top Of The Pops*, created Ziggy Stardust by the alchemical method. He bombarded various oddments of pop ephemera with genius until they formed an entirely new element: the perfect performing doppelganger or alter ego for the chameleon-like artist.

The "Stardust" portion of the name was borrowed from a singer called The Legendary Stardust Cowboy (also called "Ledge" for short, but not for long). Bowie acknowledged the debt in 2002: "He was a stablemate of mine on Mercury records in the late sixties and I chewed off the last part of his name for Ziggy, of course. When I read on his site that he thought that because I'd borrowed his name that at least I should sing one of his songs, I got guilty and wanted to make amends immediately. So I covered one of his best songs, 'I Took A Trip On A Gemini Spaceship'." But the inner essence of the Ziggy character – although certainly not the look – was inspired by a fallen rock idol. In the late fifties and early sixties, leather-clad Vince Taylor (and his backing group, The Playboys) had released a few UK singles, including 'Brand New Cadillac', before finding considerable success in France. However, by the time Bowie met him, Taylor was back home in England, spaced-out and delusional. So this song, as they say, is dedicated to absent friends and to the casualties of the Music Biz…

# 1973 Angie

Words & Music by Mick Jagger & Keith Richards

© Copyright 1973 Westminster Music Limited.
All Rights Reserved. International Copyright Secured.

**With feeling**

1. Oh Ang - ie,___ oh An - gie,___ when will those dark clouds dis -ap - pear?
*(Verses 2 & 3 see block lyrics)*

An- gie,___ An - gie,___ where will it lead us from here?___ With no
*(Verse 4 on 𝄉 see block lyrics)*

lov-ing in our souls_ and no mon-ey in our coats,_ you can't say_ we're sat-is- fied.___ But

An- gie,___ An - gie, you can't say_ we've nev-er tried.___

An- gie,___ I still love you ba - by,___ ev-'ry-where I look_ I see your eyes.___

There ain't a wom-an who_ comes close to you, come on ba - by dry your eyes.___ But

An- gie,___ An - gie, ain't it good_ to be a- live?___
An- gie,___ An - gie, they can't say_ we nev-er tried._

*Verse 2:*
Angie you're beautiful, but ain't it time we said goodbye?
Angie I still love you, remember all those nights we cried?
All the dreams we held so close, seemed to all go up in smoke;
Let me whisper in your ear, "Angie, Angie, where will it lead us from here?"

*Verse 3:*
*Instrumental for 8 bars*
Oh Angie don't you weep, ah, your kisses still taste sweet;
I hate that sadness in your eyes,
But Angie, Angie, ain't it time we said goodbye?

*Verse 4:*
*Instrumental for 4 bars*
With no loving in our souls and no money in our coats,
You can't say we're satisfied.
But Angie...

# But Angie, Angie,
# ain't it good to be alive?
## Angie, Angie, they can't say we never tried.

In all the furore about The Rolling Stones, who just keep rolling along like Old Man River (except even older) it can sometimes be forgotten that Keith Richards and Mick Jagger are a formidable team of songwriters. Thanks are due to Andrew Loog Oldham for setting them jointly to work. They could write tender: 'As Tears Go By' for the hauntingly beautiful Marianne Faithfull, 'Ruby Tuesday'; as well as tempestuous: '(I Can't Get No) Satisfaction', 'Get Off Of My Cloud', 'Jumpin Jack Flash' and so many more. 'Angie' was one of their gentler ballads, for any who may not recall that the Stones can also do wistful. And in their nth year of rolling, do they have any regrets? Well, here's a startling quote from Mick Jagger: "I wish we'd won the Eurovision Song Contest, but there's not much else I'd change." Mick Jagger, above, at Dynamic Sound Studios, Jamaica during the sessions that produced 'Angie'.

# 1973

# Cum On Feel The Noize

Words & Music by Jim Lea &
Noddy Holder
© Copyright 1973 Barn Publishing (Slade) Limited.
All Rights Reserved. International Copyright Secured.

C    G/B    Am    C    G/B    Am

cum on    feel    the    noize,_____    girls    grab    their    boys,_____    we'll get

F    C/E    G/D    F    C/E    G/D

wild,    wild,___    wild,___    we'll get    wild,    wild,___    wild.___    So

*Verse 2:*
So you think you've got a funny face,
Well that ain't no worry.
And I don't know why,
And I don't know why.
Say I'm a dropout but it's no disgrace,
But there ain't no hurry.
And I don't know why.
And I don't know why anymore, oh no.

*Verse 3:*
So you think we have a lazy time,
And you should know better.
And I don't know why,
I just don't know why.
And you say I've got a dirty mind,
Well I'm mean go-getter.
And I don't know why,
I just don't know why anymore, oh no.

Creative spelling was a trademark of Slade, and 'Cum On Feel The Noize', penned by the band's regular songwriting team of Noddy Holder and Jim Lea, upheld the tradition. Slade was primarily a live band that had made a living for years without ever recording. When they finally did get into the studio, the Wolverhampton heroes certainly knew how to generate volume and excitement, and their energetic songs with catchphrase titles were soon being heard on football terraces, in pubs and anywhere else that gusto was deemed more important than musical phrasing. No one could ever accuse Slade of pretension and 'Cum On Feel The Noize' was perhaps their most exuberantly unrestrained anthem. Slade, left to right, Jim Lea, Dave Hill, Don Powell & Noddy Holder.

# 1973

# Gaye

Words & Music by Clifford T Ward
© Copyright 1973 Edward Kassner Music Company
Limited.
All Rights Reserved. International Copyright Secured.

Slow ballad ♩ = 76

*Verse 2:*

Oh Gaye, you allay my every fear,

In a most extraordinary way,

If I thought that I could find my way without you,

I would not ask you to stay.

*Chorus 2:*

You're the tray of nice things that I upset yesterday,

The mainstay of my dreams that I let slip away,

# 1973

# 20th Century Boy

Words & Music by Marc Bolan

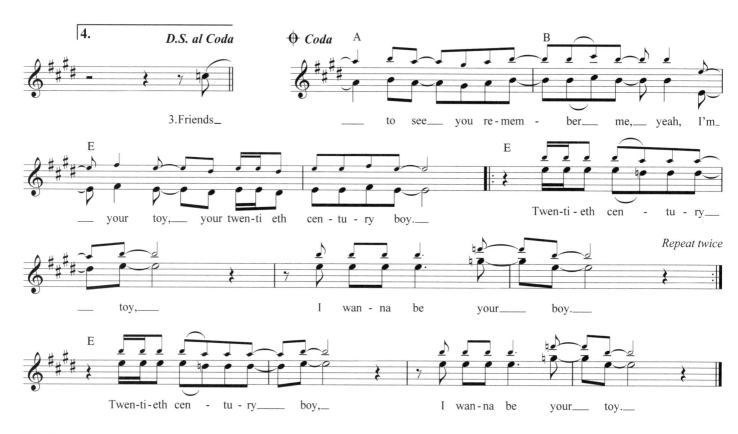

*Verse 2:*
Friends say it's fine, friends say it's good,
Everybody says it's just like rock 'n' roll.
Fly like a plane, drive like a car,
Ball like a hound, babe I wanna be your man.
Well it's plain to see you were meant for me
I'm your toy, your twentieth century boy.

*Verse 3:*
Friends say it's fine, friends say it's good,
Everybody says it's just like rock 'n' roll.
I move like a cat, charge like a ram,
Sting like a bee, babe I wanna be your man.
Well it's plain to see you were meant for me,
Yeah, I'm your toy, your twentieth century boy.

I move like a cat,

# charge like a ram,
## sting like a bee, babe, I wanna be your man.

Original one half of a rather fey folk duo Tyrannosaurus Rex, Marc Bolan effected a makeover to become the teen idol leader of abbreviated T. Rex which specialised in catchy, souped-up boogie.

# 1974

# Pick Up The Pieces

Music by Roger Ball, Alan Gorrie, Malcolm Duncan, Robert McIntosh, Omie McIntyre & Hamish Stuart

The six original members of The Average White Band were all raised in Scotland but their musical tastes and their career were to be defined by American funk, soul and disco. 'Pick Up The Pieces', written by the group, came from their second album, *AWB*, the first of several they made with producer Arif Mardin. It was an album dominated by disco music and this instrumental track featured a tenor sax solo and twin guitars. In the US 'Pick Up the Pieces' was taken to heart by young blacks and it became a million-seller and no. 1 in December 1974 despite initial resistance from some black radio stations.

Average White Band (clockwise from left) Gorrie, Ball, Duncan, Steve Ferrone who replaced original drummer, McIntosh, McIntyre and Stuart.

# The Time Warp

Words & Music by Richard O'Brien
© Copyright 1974 Druidcrest Music Limited.
All Rights Reserved. International Copyright Secured.

**Songwriter Richard O'Brien and**
*Rocky Horror* **Star Tim Curry**

It's just a jump to the left,
and then a step to the right.
With your hands on your hips,
you bring your knees in tight.

gain,____ let's do the Time Warp a - gain.____ 2. It's so

Well I was tap - ping down the street, just - a hav - ing a think,____ when a

snake of a guy____ gave me an ev - il wink.____ It shook me up,____ it took me by sur - prise;____ had a

pick - up truck____ and the dev - il's eyes.____ He stared at me____ and I felt a change;_

time meant noth - ing, nev - er would a - gain.____

*Verse 2:*
It's so dreamy, oh fantasy free me,
So you can't see me, no, not at all.
In another dimension with voyeuristic intention,
Well-secluded, I see all.
With a bit of a mind flip, you're into the time slip,
Nothing can ever be the same.
You're spaced out on sensation, like you're under sedation.
Let's do the Time Warp again, let's do the Time Warp again.

# 1975 All Around My Hat

Traditional. Arranged by Peter Knight, Maddy Prior, Tim Hart, Bob Johnson, Rick Kemp & Nigel Pegrum

*Verse 2:*

With a quarter pound of reasons,

And a half pound of sense,

A small sprig of thyme and as much of prudence,

You mix them all together,

And you will plainly see,

He's a false deluding young man,

Let him go, farewell he.

# 1975 Funky Gibbon

Words & Music by Bill Oddie
© Copyright 1975 Oddsocks Music Limited.
All Rights Reserved. International Copyright Secured.

*Come on everybody, it's gibbon time!*

**Funky** ♩ = 88

1. We're the Good-ies, how do you do? We've just been down to the zoo. We saw a mon-key in a cage

doing a dance that could be the rage. It's not hard, so let's all do the fun-ky gib-bon, ooh, ooh, ooh!

(Synthesiser)

Do, do, do, the fun-ky gib-bon. (The fun-ky gib-bon.)

We are here to show you how.__ (Ooh, ooh, ooh!) Ooh, ooh, ooh, the fun-ky gib-bon. (The fun-ky gib-bon.) He's

(Synthesiser)

just like you so come on do the fun-ky gib-bon now.

2. Dogs are al-ways howl-ing, cats are al-ways yowl-ing, but gib-bons on-ly like to sing and dance
*(Verse 3 see block lyrics)*

__ (Ooh-oob she-boo.) Please be like that mon-key, get a lit-tle fun-ky, and

in a while you'll start to smile, giv-en half a chance.__ Do, do, do, the fun-ky

gib-bon. We are here to show you how.__ (Ooh, ooh, ooh!) Ooh, ooh, ooh, the fun-ky

*Verse 3:*
Gee, the world would be good,
I know how nice it could be,
With just a little gibbon take, (sha, la, la, la),
Be just like a gibbon,
Oh, feel the rhythm,
An' you'll agree, you'll dance up to,
The planet of the apes.

'Funky Gibbon' was a spinoff from a BBC comedy series *The Goodies*, a show that combined cartoon-style humour with light satire and slapstick. One of its three mainstays, Bill Oddie brought unexpectedly high musical aspirations to recording this novelty song. "I started off – it's almost unbelievable considering how stupid the song is – trying to get the feel of a Miles Davis track," he recalls. In the end the recording was made with keyboard player Dave Macrae playing clavinet and synth-bass, with Oddie whacking the top of a grand piano and a horn section dubbed on top. "The idea that all that effort went into 'Funky Gibbon'…" Oddie reflected after the event. "It sounds like Parliament on a bad day."

The Goodies, left to right, Bill Oddie, Graeme Garden & Tim Brooke Taylor.

Please be like that monkey,
## get a little funky,
and in a while you'll start to smile,
## given half the chance.

10CC was formed in 1970 from some of the brightest talents on the Manchester pop scene. Clockwise from top, Kevin Godley, Graham Gouldman, Lol Crème and Eric Stewart.

# I'm Not In Love

Words & Music by Eric Stewart & Graham Gouldman

**Verse 2:**

I like to see you, but then again,
That doesn't mean you mean that much to me.
So if I call you, don't make a fuss;
Don't tell your friends about the two of us.
I'm not in love, no, no, it's because...

# 1975

# Make Me Smile (Come Up And See Me)

Words & Music by Steve Harley
© Copyright 1975 RAK Publishing Limited.
All Rights Reserved. International Copyright Secured.

la, la, la.　Ooh,_____ la, la, la.　Come up and see__

__ me,　make me　smile,_____　I'll do what you want,__

__　run - ning　wild._____

*Verse 2:*
There's nothing left,
All is gone and run away,
Maybe you'll tarry for a while,
It's just a test,
A game for us to play,
Win or lose, it's hard to smile.

Resist, resist,
It's from yourself you'll have to hide,

Come up and see me to make me smile,
I'll do what you want, running wild.

*Verse 3:*
There ain't no more,
You've taken everything,
From my belief in Mother Earth,
Can you ignore my faith in everything,
'Cause I know what faith is,
And what it's worth.

Away, away,
And don't say maybe you'll try,

To come up and see me, to make me smile,
I'll do what you want, running wild.

**Steve Harley was a former newspaper reporter who fronted Cockney Rebel and made headlines through some outspoken interviews.**

# 1975

# The Man With The Child In His Eyes

Words & Music by Kate Bush
© Copyright 1975 Kate Bush Music Limited/EMI Music Publishing Limited.
All Rights Reserved. International Copyright Secured.

**Flowing**

1. I hear___ him___ be-fore___ I go to sleep,___ and foc-us___ on the
*(Verse 2 see block lyrics)*
day that's been. I re-a-lise___ he's there___ when I turn the light off, and turn
ov-er.___ No-bod-y knows___ ab-out___ my man. They think he's lost on___ some
___ hor-i-zon.___ And sud-den-ly___ I find___ my-self list-'ning to a man___
___ I've nev-er known bef-ore, tell-ing me a-bout___ the sea,___ all___ his loves___ to et-
-er-nit-y.___ *Chorus:* Ooh,_____ he's here a-gain:___
the man___ with the child in his eyes. Ooh,_____ he's here a-gain:___

**1.** the man___ with the child in his eyes.

**2.** eyes.

*Verse 2:*
He's very understanding, and he's so aware of all my situations,
And when I stay up late, he's always waiting,
But I feel him hesitate,
Oh, I'm so worried about my love, they say no, no, it won't last forever,
And here I am again my girl, wondering what on earth I'm doing here,
Maybe he doesn't love me, I just took a trip on my love for him.

# Ooh,

he's here again:
the man with the child in his eyes.

Kate Bush's weird songs enlivened the seventies but always resisted interpretation. 'The Man With The Child In His Eyes' was taken from her album *The Kick Inside* which had already given her a big hit with 'Wuthering Heights'. However, the song had been recorded even earlier on a demo when she was only sixteen. Rumoured to be susceptible to older men, Kate, above, said of the song: "The inspiration … was really just a particular thing that happened when I went to the piano. The piano just started speaking to me. It was a theory that I had had for a while that I just observed in most of the men that I know: the fact that they just are little boys inside and how wonderful it is that they manage to retain this magic."

# You Sexy Thing

Words & Music by Errol Brown
© Copyright 1975 RAK Publishing Limited.
All Rights Reserved. International Copyright Secured.

**Laid-back** ♩ = 108

I bel-ieve in mir-a- cles,___ where're you from,___ you sex-y thing?_____

I bel-ieve in mir-a- cles,___ since you came a- long,_____ you sex-y thing.___

_____ 1. Where did you come_ from ba - by? How did you know_ I need-
*(Verse 2 see block lyrics)*

- ed you?_ How did you know___ I need - ed you_ so bad - ly?___

How did you know___ I'd give my heart_ glad - ly?___ Yes - ter - day___ I was

one of the lone - ly peop - le, now you're ly-ing close_ to me, mak-ing love to me.__

I bel-ieve in mir-a- cles,___ where're you from,___ you sex-y thing?_____

*Repeat to fade*

I bel-ieve in mir-a- cles,___ since you came a long,_____ you sex-y thing._____

*Verse 2:*
Where did you come from angel? How did you know I'd be the one?
Did you know you're everything I prayed for? Did you know every night and day for?
Every day need love and satisfaction,
Now you're lying next to me, giving it to me.

Errol Brown, centre with Hot Chocolate, was fortunate to receive personal permission from John Lennon to record a reggae version of 'Give Peace A Chance' – it was even released on the Apple label, with the artists originally credited as The Hot Chocolate Band. Later, as the snappier-sounding Hot Chocolate, they enjoyed a succession of chart successes written by Brown himself, becoming the only UK group at that time to notch up hits in fifteen consecutive years. 'You Sexy Thing' was the most enduring, and was granted a kind of immortality when it was prominently featured in the smash-hit British film, *The Full Monty*. Errol Brown was awarded the MBE by Her Majesty the Queen, and also won an Ivor Novello Award for his outstanding contribution to British music.

I believe in miracles,
# where're you from
you sexy thing?

# 1976

# The Boys Are Back In Town

Words & Music by Phil Lynott
© Copyright 1976 Pippin The Friendly Ranger Music Company Limited.
Universal Music Publishing Limited.
All Rights Reserved. International Copyright Secured.

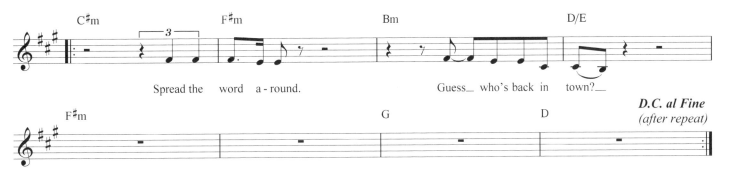

Spread the word a-round.                    Guess__ who's back in town?__

**D.C. al Fine**
*(after repeat)*

Verse 2:
You know that chick that used to dance a lot?
Every night she'd be on the floor shaking what she'd got,
Man, when I tell you she was cool, she was red hot,
I mean she was steamin',
And that time over at Johnny's place,
Well this chick got up and she slapped Johnny's face,
Man, we just fell about the place,
If that chick don't want to know, forget her.

Verse 3:
Friday night and they'll be dressed to kill,
Down at Dino's Bar and Grill,
The drink will flow and blood will spill,
But if the boys want to fight you'd better let 'em,
That jukebox in the corner blastin' out my favourite songs,
The nights are getting warmer; it won't be long,
Won't be long 'til summer comes,
Now that the boys are here again.

**Thin Lizzie leader Phil Lynott played bass on stage but composed on a regular guitar.**

# 1976

# Don't Cry For Me Argentina

Music by Andrew Lloyd Webber
Lyrics by Tim Rice
(c) Copyright 1976 & 1977 Evita Music Limited.
All Rights Reserved. International Copyright Secured.

**Slowly**

1. It won't be ea - sy, you'll think it strange, when I try to ex-plain how I

*(Verses 2 & 3 see block lyrics)*

feel, that I still need your love af - ter all that I've done:_____ you won't be - lieve me,

all you will see is a girl you once knew, al - though she's dressed up to the nines, at

**Slow Tango feel**

six - es and sev - ens with you. Don't cry for me Ar - gen - ti - na,_____ the

*(Instrumental on ％)*

truth is I nev - er left you: all through my wild days, my mad ex - is - tence, I kept my

**To Codas** ⊕                    **D.C. al Coda 1**        ⊕ **Coda 1**

prom - ise, don't keep your dis - tance._____            dis - tance._

Have I said too much? There's noth-ing more I can think of to say to you.        But

**rit.**                    **D.S. al Coda 2**        ⊕ ⊕ **Coda 2**

all you have to do is look at me to know that ev -'ry word is true.        dis - tance.____

**Verse 2:**
I had to let it happen, I had to change,
Couldn't stay all my life down at heel,
Looking out of the window, staying out of the sun.
So I chose freedom,
Running around trying everything new,
But nothing impressed me at all;
I never expected it to.

**Verse 3:**
And as for fortune and as for fame,
I never invited them in,
Though it seemed to the world they were all I desired.
They are illusions,
They're not the solutions they promised to be,
The answer was here all the time;
I love you and hope you love me.

Don't cry for me, Argentina,
the truth is I never left you:
all through my wild days,
my mad existence,
I kept my promise,
# don't keep your distance.

Tim Rice, left, and Andrew Lloyd Webber, right, turned several hallowed conventions of musical theatre upside down. In earlier years, the show invariably came first, presenting to the public a musical score which would hopefully yield one or more hit songs. However, in a record-buying age, these bright lads realised there was no better advance publicity for a new stage musical than a hit song in the charts. Furthermore, another convention had decreed that any song destined for "take-home-hit" status needed to work independently of the theatrical storyline. And yet 'Don't Cry For Me, Argentina' (which is full of lyric images highly specific to the show) became a number one chart hit for Julie Covington, long before *Evita* had even been staged.

Tim Rice also introduced an entirely new voice to theatre lyrics: quirky, conversational, irreverent and contemporary; the perfect blending of pop and showbiz sensibilities.

After a sensationally successful partnership, Tim Rice and Andrew Lloyd Webber reached a parting of the ways. Both would find further glory with other collaborators: Tim wrote *Chess* with Benny Andersson and Bjorn Ulvaeus (from Abba) and a succession of Oscar-winning songs for Disney animated movies with Alan Menken and Elton John. He also wrote songs with John Barry, Burt Bacharach and Mike Batt (and that's just the "B"s!) as well as publishing books on pop music and cricket. As we go to press, Rice and Lloyd Webber are back in harness together working on the London revival of *Evita*.

According to his self-penned and self-deprecating biography: "He has won many awards, mainly for the wrong things, or for simply turning up… Tim Rice wanted to be Elvis. Then he met Andrew Lloyd Webber whose musical ambitions were in theatre rather than rock. They joined forces as one could knock out a decent tune, the other had a way with words. They wrote four shows together. The first… was never performed, but *Joseph And The Amazing Technicolor Dreamcoat*, *Jesus Chris Superstar* and *Evita* became, and indeed remain, hugely successful all around the world, on both stage and screen. Feeling certain that they could never top this lot, the pair went their separate ways in the early eighties, whereupon ALW immediately topped that lot with *Cats*."

Joan Armatrading

JOAN ARMATRADING

# 1976

# Love And Affection

Words & Music by Joan Armatrading

Ballad ♩ = 88

I am not in love___ but I'm op-en to per-sua- sion. East or West,___

___ where's the best___ for rom- anc - ing?___ With a friend I can smile

but with a lov-er I could hold my head___ back, I could real-ly laugh, real-ly laugh. Thank you,___

___ you took me danc - ing___ 'cross the floor, cheek to cheek.___

___ But with a lov-er I could real-ly move,___ real-ly move. I could real-ly dance,___ real-ly dance,___ real-ly dance.

Real-ly dance,___ I could real-ly move,___ real-ly move, real-ly move.___ real-ly move.___ Now if I can feel the sun

___ in my eyes___ and the rain on my face, why can't___ I___ feel___

love?___ I can real-ly love,___ real-ly love,___ real-ly love,___

real - ly love,___ real-ly love.___ Love, love, love love,___ love.

# 1976  Music

Words & Music by John Miles
© Copyright 1976 RAK Publishing Limited.
All Rights Reserved. International Copyright Secured.

# 1977

# How Deep Is Your Love?

Words & Music by Barry Gibb,
Maurice Gibb & Robin Gibb
© Copyright 1977 Gibb Brothers Music/Crompton
Songs.
BMG Music Publishing Limited (66.66%)/ Warner/
Chappell Music Limited (33.34%).

**Moderately**

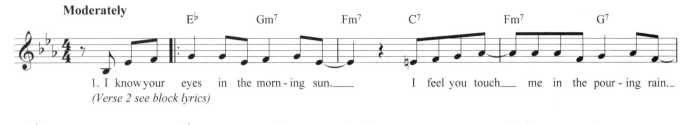

1. I know your eyes in the morn-ing sun.___ I feel you touch___ me in the pour-ing rain.___
*(Verse 2 see block lyrics)*

___ And the mo - ment that you wan-der far___ from me, I wan-na feel you in my arms a-gain.___

___ And you come___ to me___ on a sum - mer breeze;___ keep me warm___ in your love,___ then you soft-

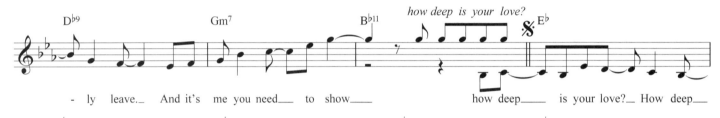

- ly leave.___ And it's me you need___ to show___ how deep___ is your love?___ How deep___

___ is your___ love? I real - ly mean___ to learn.___ 'Cause we're liv-ing in a world of fools,___

___ break-ing us down, when they all___ should let us be,___ we be-long___

___ to you___ and me.

*D.S. and fade*

How deep___

*Verse 2:*

I believe in you.
You know the door to my very soul.
You're the light in my deepest, darkest hour;
You're my saviour when I fall.
And you may not think I care for you
When you know down inside that I really do.
And it's me you need to show
How deep is your love?

# 1977
# Mr. Blue Sky

Words & Music by Jeff Lynne
© Copyright 1977 EMI Songs Limited.
All Rights Reserved. International Copyright Secured.

# 1977

# Mull Of Kintyre

Words & Music by Paul McCartney
& Denny Laine
© Copyright 1977 MPL Communications Limited.
All Rights Reserved. International Copyright Secured.

# We Are The Champions

Words & Music by Freddie Mercury
© Copyright 1977 Queen Music Limited.
All Rights Reserved. International Copyright Secured.

Ah, we are the champ - ions, we are the champ - ions,

no time for los - ers 'cause we are the champ - ions.

*Verse 2:*
I've taken my bows and my curtain calls,
You've brought me fame and fortune and everything that goes with it; I thank you all.
But it's been no bed of roses, no pleasure cruise,
I consider it a challenge before all human race,
And I ain't gonna lose.

**Now celebrated as a football anthem, 'We Are The Champions' reached number two in 1977 and Queen climaxed their epoch making Live Aid set with the song in 1985. Left to right, John Deacon Freddie Mercury & Brian May.**

# 1978

# Baker Street

Words & Music by Gerry Rafferty
© Copyright 1978 Icon Music Limited.
Universal Music Publishing Limited.
All Rights Reserved. International Copyright Secured.

so ea-sy but you're try - ing, you're try - ing now.___

An - oth - er year and then you'll be hap - py, just one more year and then you'll be hap - py, but

*To Coda* ⊕      *D.S. al Coda* (with repeat)

you're cry - ing, you're cry - ing now.___

⊕ *Coda*

*Sax solo*

*Repeat to fade*

*Verse 2:*

Way down the street there's a man in his place.
He opens the door, he's got that look on his face.
And he asks you where you've been;
You tell him who you've seen and you talk about anything.
He's got his dream about buying some land;
He's gonna give up the booze and the one-night stands.
And then he'll settle down in some quiet little town,
And forget about everything.

But you know he'll always keep moving;
You know he's never gonna stop moving.
His heels rolling:
He's a rolling stone.
And when you wake up it's a new morning;
The sun is shining, it's a new morning.
And you're going,
You're going home.

# Another crazy day, you'll drink the night away
## and forget about everything.

Gerry Rafferty's song of yearning for a better life is one of his best known and his recording of it is distinguished by Raphael Ravenscroft's iconic saxophone solo. In 1978 Rafferty was already an alumnus of Stealers Wheel and an earlier folk duo, The Humblebums, where he partnered Billy Connolly. 'Baker Street' was the standout track on Rafferty's *City To City* album and has since become a radio airplay staple. Undercover and The Foo Fighters have both covered the song.

# 1978

# Bright Eyes

Words & Music by Mike Batt
© Copyright 1978 Watership Productions Limited.
EMI Songs Limited.
All Rights Reserved. International Copyright Secured.

**Dreamily** ♩ = 56

1. Is it a kind of___ dream?___ Float-ing out___ on the tide,___
*(Verses 2, 3 & 4 see block lyric)*

foll-ow-ing the riv-er of death_ down stream_ or is it a dream? 2. There's a mean? Oh,___ is it a

dream? Bright_ eyes,___ burn-ing_ like_ fire,_ bright_ eyes,___ how can you close and fail?

*To Coda*

How can the light_ that burned so bright-ly sud-den-ly burn_ so pale?_ Bright_ eyes._

*(Oboe solo)*

*D.C. al Coda*
*(with repeat)*

*Coda*

___ Bright_ eyes.___ burn-ing_ like_ fire,_ bright_ eyes,___ how can you close_ and fail?

___ How can the light_ that burned so bright-ly sud-den-ly burn_ so pale?_ Bright_ eyes.___

*Verse 2:*
There's a fog along the horizon,
A strange glow in the sky,
And nobody seems to know where you go,
And what does it mean? Oh, is it a dream?

*Verse 3:*
Is it a kind of shadow?
Reaching into the night,
Wandering over the hills unseen,
Or is it a dream?

*Verse 4:*
There's a high wind in the trees,
A cold sound in the air,
And nobody knows when you go,
And where do you start, oh, into the dark?

# 1978 | English Rose

Words & Music by Paul Weller
© Copyright 1978 Stylist Music Limited/BMG Music
Publishing Limited.
All Rights Reserved. International Copyright Secured.

**In a relaxed manner**  ♩ = 114

No mat-ter where I roam,— I will re-turn— to my Eng-lish Rose.— For no—

— bonds can ev - er tempt— me from— she.

1. I sailed the sev - en seas,— flown the whole blue sky,—

*(Verses 2 & 3 see block lyrics)*

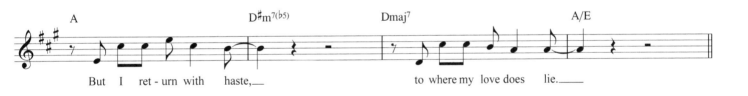

But I ret - urn with haste,— to where my love does lie.—

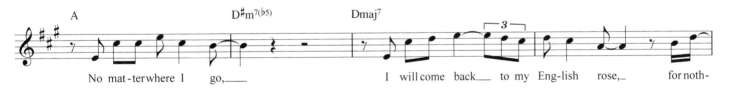

No mat-ter where I go,— I will come back— to my Eng-lish rose,— for noth-

*Repeat twice*

- ing can ev - er tempt— me from— she.

*Verse 2:*                                    *Verse 3:*

Verse 2:
I've searched the secret mists,
I've climbed the highest peaks,
And caught the wild wind home,
To hear a soft voice speak.

Verse 3:
I've been to ancient worlds,
I've searched the whole universe,
Aboard the first train home,
To be at her side.

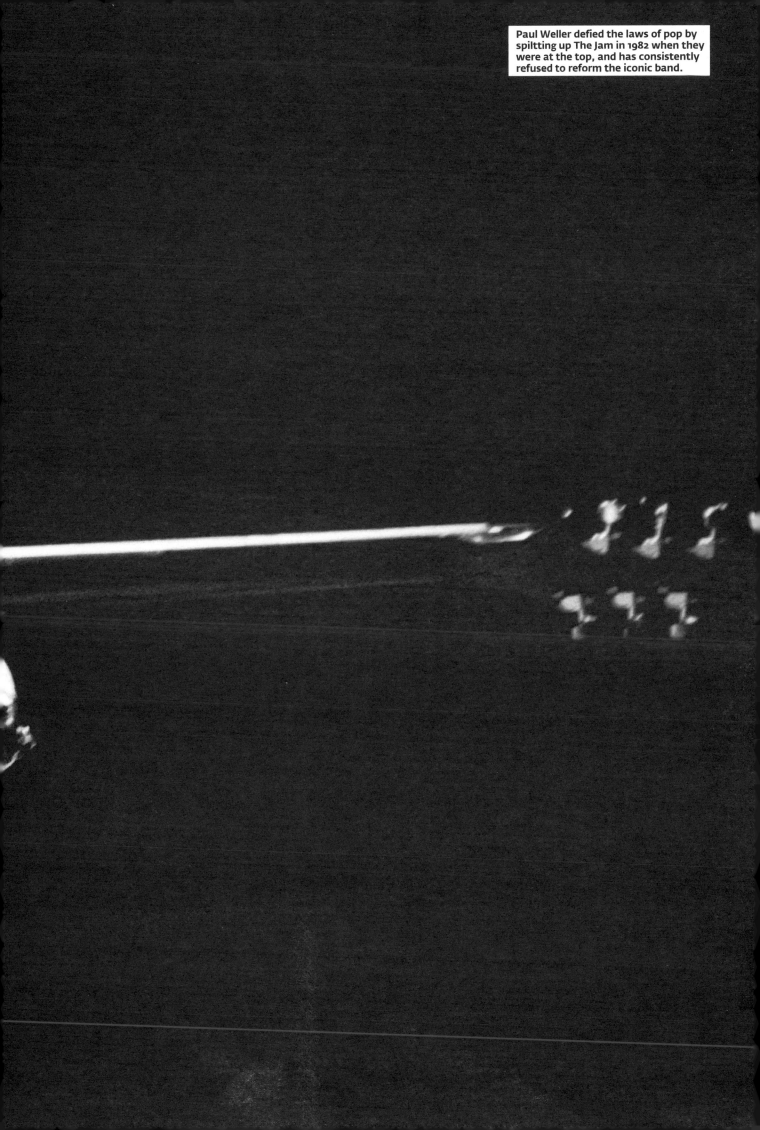

Paul Weller defied the laws of pop by spiltting up The Jam in 1982 when they were at the top, and has consistently refused to reform the iconic band.

# 1978

# Ever Fallen In Love (With Someone You Shouldn't've)

Words & Music by Pete Shelley
© Copyright 1978 Complete Music Limited.
All Rights Reserved. International Copyright Secured.

with?  Ev - er  fal - len in love___ with?

Ev - er  fal - len in love_ with some-one___ you shouldn't-'ve fal - len in love___ with?___

*Verse 2:*
I can't see much of a future,
Unless we find out what's to blame; what a shame,
And we won't be together much longer
Unless we realise that we are the same.

*Verse 3:*
You disturb my natural emotions,
You make me feel like dirt and that hurts,
And if I start a commotion,
I'll only end up losing you and that's worse.

**Manchester's Buzzcocks combined the energy of punk with a melodic twist that came to be known as power pop. Pictured here are singer Pete Shelley and bassist Steve Garvey.**

# 1978

# Forever Autumn

Words by Paul Vigrass & Gary Osborne
Music by Jeff Wayne

1. The sum-mer sun____ is fad - ing as the year grows old,

*(Verse 2 see block lyrics)*

and dark - er days____ are draw - ing____ near.____

____ will be____ much cold - er,____ now you're not____ here.____

The win-ter winds.

Like the sun through the trees____ you came____ to love____ me,____

like a leaf on a breeze____ you blew____ a - way.

3. Through aut-umn's gold - en gown____ we used to kick our way;____

*(Verse 4 see block lyrics)*

you al-ways loved____ this time____ of____ year.

Those fall-en leaves____

*Verse 2:*
I watch the birds fly south across the autumn sky,
And one by one they disappear.
I wish that I was flying with them,
Now you're not here.

*Verse 4:*
A gentle rain falls softly on my weary eyes,
As if to hide a lonely tear.
My life will be forever autumn,
'Cause you're not here, 'cause you're not here, 'cause you're not here.

# 1978

# Hit Me With Your Rhythm Stick

Words & Music by Ian Dury & Chas Jankel

**Verse 2:**
In the wilds of Borneo,
And the vineyards of Bordeaux
Eskimo, Arapaho,
Move their body to and fro.

*Chorus:*
Hit me with your rhythm stick, hit me, hit me!
Das ist gut, c'est fantastique, hit me, hit me, hit me!
Hit me with your rhythm stick,
Nice to be a lunatic,
Hit me, hit me, hit me!

**Verse 3:**
In the desert of Tiger Bay,
On the road to Mandalay,
From Bombay, down Dagenham Heathway,
Over the hills and far away.

*Chorus:*
Hit me with your rhythm stick, hit me, hit me!
C'est si bon, es ist nicht, hit me, hit me, hit me!
Hit me with your rhythm stick,
Two fat persons, click, click, click,
Hit me, hit me, hit me!

Hit me with your rhythm stick,

# hit me! Hit me!

Je t'adore, ich liebe dich,
hit me! Hit me! Hit me!

Ian Dury, above, and the Blockheads purveyed a bizarrely life-affirming brand of cockney chutzpah, mixing manic music-hall energy with jazz and punk overtones. They influenced a number of later bands including Madness. Dury skewered the zeitgeist with a string of lyrics in spectacular vernacular, coining the phrase "sex, drugs & rock 'n' roll" and listing his idiosyncratic 'Reasons To Be Cheerful':

"A bit of grin and bear it, a bit of come and share it,
You're welcome – we can spare it – and yellow socks…"

"Too short to be haughty, too nutty to be naughty," Ian Dury was fearless about referring to disability in his lyrics (he was himself a polio sufferer). In 1998, he and Robbie Williams travelled as UNICEF ambassadors to Sri Lanka to promote the importance of polio vaccination for children.

"I've always said that if I write a lyric that's okay, it'll get off the table, go out on the street, hail a cab and go down Denmark Street and make me a few quid. It's like doing the pools, there's always that element of excitement." – Ian Dury

# 1978

# Oliver's Army

Words & Music by Elvis Costello
© Copyright 1978 BMG Music Publishing Limited.
All Rights Reserved. International Copyright Secured.

**Moderately**

1.Don't start me talk - ing; I could talk all night.
*(Verse 2 see block lyrics)*

— My mind goes sleep - walk - ing while I'm put - ting the world to right.

— Called car - eers in - for - ma - tion. Have you got your - self an oc - cu - pa -

Ol - i - ver's ar - my is here to stay. Ol - i - ver's ar - my are on their way.
- tion?

— And I would rath - er be an - y - where else than here to -

**1.**
- day.

**2.**
Hong - Kong is up for grabs,—

Lon - don is full of— A - rabs. We could be in Pal - es - tine,—

Geeky Elvis Costello rose to fame on the punk tide of anger and aggression but in reality was a pop singer and songwriter with more traditional values.

o - ver run__ by a Chin - ese line with the boys from the Mer-sey and the Thames and the Tyne.__

__ But there's no dan - ger. It's a prof-

- es - sion - al__ car - eer, though it could be ar - ranged__ with just a word__ in Mis-

- ter Church - ill's ear.__ If you're out of luck__ or out__ of__ work__ we could send you to__

__ Jo - han - nes - burg. Ol - i - ver's ar - my is

here to stay.__ Ol - i - ver's ar - my are on their way.__ And I would rath-er be an - y-where

else than__ here to - day. And I would rath-er be an-y-where else than__ here to -

*Repeat to fade*

- day.__ Oh, oh, oh, oh,__ oh, oh, oh,__
oh,__

*Verse 2:*
There was a checkpoint Charlie,
He didn't crack a smile,
But it's no laughing party when you've been put on Murder Mile,
Only takes one itchy trigger,
One more widow, one less white nigger.

# Sultans Of Swing

Words & Music by Mark Knopfler
© Copyright 1978 Straitjacket Songs Limited.
All Rights Reserved. International Copyright Secured.

sound.                    Way on down_ south,              way on     down__ south

Lon-don town.        (Guitar)

**1.**     3. You check out          **2.**     5. And a    crowd of young_ boys, they're
*(Verse 6 see block lyrics)*

fool-in' a-round_ in the cor  -  ner,          drunk and dressed in their best  brown bag-gies and_their plat-form_

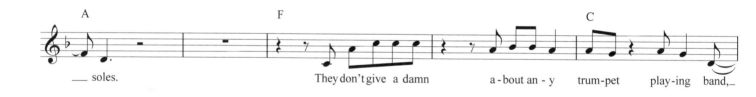

__ soles.                    They don't give a damn     a-bout an - y   trum-pet   play-ing   band,_

_____        it ain't what   they call   rock and  roll._   (Guitar)

*To Coda*

And the Sul - tans,_                    yeah, the  Sul - tans_  are play-ing

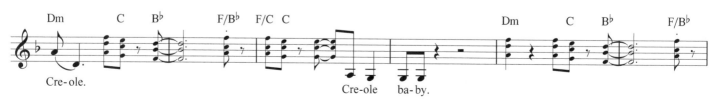

Cre-ole.                    Cre-ole   ba-by.

*D.S. al Coda*          *Coda*

F/C    C

Ah,  ah.

Dm          C

swing.___

B♭          F/B♭          F/C    C

*Repeat to fade*

*Verse 3:*
You check out Guitar George,
He knows all the chords,
Mind, he's strictly rhythm,
He doesn't want to make it cry or sing,
When he gets up under the lights to play his thing.

*Verse 4:*
And Harry doesn't mind,
If he doesn't make the scene,
He's got a daytime job,
He's doing alright,
He can play the honky-tonk just like anything,
Saving it up, Friday night sound,
With the Sultans,
With the Sultans of swing.

*Verse 6:*
And then the man he steps right up to the microphone,
And says at last,
Just as the time bell rings,
"Goodnight, now it's time to go home",
And he makes it fast with one more thing,
We are the Sultans,
We are the Sultans of swing.

In 1978 this atmospheric Mark Knopfler, left, song signalled a shift away from disco while at the same time completely ignoring the burgeoning punk movement. Knopfler has always favoured narrative lyrics and this first outing for Dire Straits told the story of a working-class jazz group who are more interested in playing distinctive music than becoming famous. Arguably Knopfler's own group went on to do both, culminating in the massive-selling *Brothers In Arms* album before he finally became a solo artist and gravitated towards guitar duets with the likes of Les Paul and Chet Atkins, and intermittent joint ventures with country singers such as George Jones, Willie Nelson and Emmylou Harris.

# 1978 | Teenage Kicks

Words & Music by John O'Neill
© Copyright 1978 West Bank Songs Limited.
Universal/MCA Music Limited.
All Rights Reserved. International Copyright Secured.

**With a strong beat** ♩ = 135

1. A teen-age dream's so hard to beat__ ev-'ry time she walks__ down the street.__

A-no-ther girl in the neigh-bour-hood,__ wish she was mine, she looks so good.__

I wan-na hold her wan-na hold her tight, get teen-age kicks__ right through the night.__

2. I'm gon-na call her on the te-le-phone,__ have her o-ver 'cause I'm all a-lone.__

I need ex-cite-ment, oh, I need it bad__ and she's the best I've ev-er had.__

I wan-na hold her, wan-na hold her tight,__ get teen-age kicks__ right through the night.__ Al-right!

I wan-na hold her, wan-na

hold her tight, get teen-age kicks__ right through the night.__

# 1979

# Cars

Words & Music by Gary Numan
© Copyright 1979 Beggars Banquet Music Limited.
Universal/Momentum Music Limited.
All Rights Reserved. International Copyright Secured.

**With a driving rhythm** ♩ = 130

A

1. Here in my car___ I feel saf - est of all.___ I can lock up my doors,___ it's the

*(Verses 2, 3 & 4 see block lyrics)*

G                                                                                    D

on - ly way to live,___ in cars.___

*(synthesiser)*

**1.**          **2.** *D.C. al Fine*
*(with repeats)* A

G          *Repeat to fade*

*Verse 2:*
Here in my car, I can only receive,
I can listen to you, it keeps me stable for nights, in cars.

*Verse 4:*
Here in my car, I know I've started to think,
About leaving tonight, although nothing seems right, in cars.

*Verse 3:*
Here in my car, where the image breaks down,
Will you visit me please, if I open my door, in cars.

Tubeway Army was the first post-punk band to have an electronic hit ('Are "Friends" Electric?') but the group had really consisted only of ex-Slough grammar school boy Gary Webb aided by a variable alliance of other musicians. With 'Cars' and its parent album *The Pleasure Principle*, Gary redubbed himself Numan (a name he plucked from the *Yellow Pages*) and went solo. The song perfectly complemented its creator's stage image which seemed to be that of an android who had mislaid the anti-depressants. Numan, right, explained the song's origins thus: "I was in traffic in London once and had a problem with some people in front. They tried to beat me up and get me out of the car. I locked the doors and eventually drove up on the pavement and got away from them. It's kind of to do with that. It explains how you can feel safe inside a car in the modern world..."

# Comfortably Numb

Words & Music by Roger Waters & David Gilmour

© Copyright 1979 Warner/Chappell Music Limited (50%)/Pink Floyd Music Publishers Limited (50%). All Rights Reserved. International Copyright Secured.

I __ can't ex- plain, you would not un - der - stand;__ this is not how__ I __ am.

I_____ have be - come__ com - fort -'bly numb.

*Verse 2:*
Ok, just a little pinprick.
There'll be no more aaarrrrrgggggghhh!
But you may feel a little sick.

Can you stand up?
I do believe it's working, good.
That'll keep you going for the show.
Come on, it's time to go.

There is no pain, you are receding.
A distant ship's smoke on the horizon.
You are only coming through in waves.
Your lips move, but I can't hear what you're sayin'.
When I was a child I caught a fleeting glimpse,
Out of the corner of my eye.
I turned to look, but it was gone.
I cannot put my finger on it now.
The child is grown, the dream is gone.
I have become comfortably numb.

**Always overshadowed by the stage props and lighting at their concerts, Pink Floyd's need for anonymity reached an apogee in 1979 with The Wall, during which a wall was constructed between them and their audience. 'Comfortable Numb', a song from The Wall, was covered by The Scissor Sisters in 2005.**

# 1979

# I Don't Like Mondays

Words & Music by Bob Geldof

Bob Geldof's work for African charities has always overshadowed his role as lead singer in Dublin's Boomtown Rats.

*Verse 2:*

The telex machine is kept so clean and it types to a waiting world.

And mother feels so shocked, father's world is rocked,

And their thoughts turn to their own little girl.

Sweet sixteen, ain't that peachy keen

Now it ain't so neat to admit defeat.

They can see no reasons, 'cause there are no reasons.

What reasons do you need?

# 1979 Rabbit

Words & Music by Chas Hodges &
Dave Peacock
© Copyright 1979 Snout Music Limited.
All Rights Reserved. International Copyright Secured.

ear - holes too,___ with your in - ces - sant___ talk - in',___ you're be - com - ing a pest.___

F      "Rabbit, rabbit...*etc.*"                                *Repeat twice*

*Verse 2:*
Now you've got lovely eyes,
You've got lovely thighs;
You've got a lovely face,
You've got taste;
You've got the lovely lips,
You've got lovely hips.
But there's something else I want you to know,
I'm givin' you the elbow, 'cause...

*Verse 3:*
Now you're a wonderful girl,
You've got a wonderful smell;
You've got wonderful arms,
You've got charms;
You've got a wonderful hair,
We make a wonderful pair.
Now I don't mind 'avin' a chat,
But you have to keep givin' it that, no...

Chas Hodges, left, and Dave Peacock paid their dues in dozens of British bands in the sixties before emerging with their unique brand of 'Rockney' music which combined rock with Cockney.

# 1979 Up The Junction

Words & Music by Chris Difford &
Glenn Tilbrook
© Copyright 1979 Deptford Songs.
Rondor Music (London) Limited.
All Rights Reserved. International Copyright Secured.

**Moderately**

1. I nev-er thought it would hap - pen with me and a girl from Clap-ham out on the win-dy

*(Verse 2 see block lyrics)*

com-mon. That night I ain't for-got-ten. When she dealt out the rat-ions with some or oth-er

pas-sions, I said,"You are a la-dy". "Per - haps,"she said, "I may be."_____

3. I got a job with Stan-ley, he said I'd come in han-dy, and start-ed me on Mon-day, so I had a bath on

Sun-day. I worked el - e-ven hou-rs and bought the girl some flow-ers. She said she'd seen a doc-tor, and noth-ing now

could stop her._____ I worked all through the win-ter, the weath-er brass and

bit-ter. I put a-way a ten-ner each week to make her bet-ter. And when the time was read-y we had to sell the

tel - ly, make eve-nings by the fi - re and lit-tle kicks in-side her._____

4. This morn-ing at four - fif-ty, I took her rath-er nif-ty, down to an in-cu-bat-or. 'Bout thir-ty min-utes

lat-er, she gave birth to a daugh-ter, with-in a year a walk-er. She looked just like her moth-er, if there could be

an - oth - er._____                    5. And now she's two years old - er,    her moth-er's with a
                                         *(Verse 6 see block lyrics)*

sol - dier.    She left me when my drink-ing,    be-came a pro-per sting-ing.    The dev-il came and took me,    from bar to street to

book-ie,    no more nights by the tel-ly.    No more nights nap-pie smel-ling._____

*Verse 2:*
We moved into a basement,
With thoughts of our engagement,
We stayed in by the telly,
Although the room was smelly,
We spent our time just kissing,
The railway arms were missing,
But love had got us hooked up,
And all our time, it took up.

*Verse 6:*
Alone here in the kitchen,
I feel there's something missing,
I'd beg for some forgiveness,
But begging's not my business,
And she must write a letter,
Although I always tell her,
And so it's my assumption,
I'm really up the junction.

The devil came and took me,
# from bar to street to bookie...

Written by Squeeze's song writing team, guitarist/singers Glenn Tilbrook and Chris Difford, 'Up The Junction' is typical of the band's output at the time: simple narrative, informal rhymes ("I never thought it would happen/ With me and the girl from Clapham") and a great tune. The title finds its origins in Nell Dunn's gritty 1968 novel of the same name, which later became a BBC TV play and finally a film with Dennis Waterman and Suzy Kendall. The south London setting was retained for Squeeze's vernacular song of love found and love lost in SW11.

Their keyboard player Jools Holland went on to become a successful TV presenter of rock shows.

Above, left to right, Glen Tilbrook, Harry Kakoulli, Jools Holland, Paul Gunn and Chris Difford.

# When routine bites hard,
and ambitions are low,
and resentment rides high,
but emotions won't grow.

Joy Division

Written and performed by Joy Division, this bleak song was first recorded in 1979 as one of the BBC's John Peel Sessions in Maida Vale, West London…and then again at a live performance at Les Bains Douches, Paris. The official single version was only put on vinyl in 1980 and its release coincided with the death of the band's leading light Ian Curtis. Curtis hanged himself in the kitchen of his Macclesfield home while the band was resting between European and American tours. Iggy Pop's 'The Idiot' was found on his turntable and there was an unequivocal note which read "at this very moment, I wish I were dead. I just can't cope anymore". The three remaining members and a new fourth member regrouped as New Order during early 1981.

Half of the writing and composing team, Ian Curtis, right, and Bernard Sumner.

# 1980 | Love Will Tear Us Apart

Words & Music by Ian Curtis, Peter Hook, Bernard Sumner & Stephen Morris

**Moderately** ♩ = 144

When rou-tine bites___ hard, and am - bi-tions are___ low,
(Verses 2, 3 see block lyric)
and res-

-ent-ment rides_____ high,___ but em - o - tions won't grow, and we're

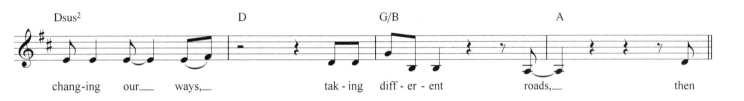

chang-ing our___ ways,___ tak - ing diff - er - ent roads,___ then

love, love will tear___ us a - part a - gain.

Love, love will tear___ us a - part a - gain.

*Repeat to fade*

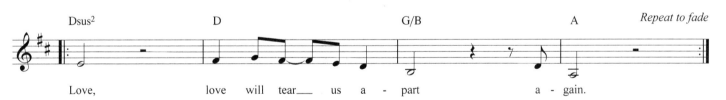

Love, love will tear___ us a - part a - gain.

*Verse 2:*
Do you cry out in your sleep?
All my feelings exposed,
Get a taste in my mouth,
As desperation takes hold,
Is it something so good?
Just can't function no more,
And love, love will tear us apart again. *(x 2)*

*Verse 3:*
Why is this bedroom so cold?
Turned away on your side,
Is my timing that flawed;
Our respect run that dry,
Yet there's still this appeal,
That we've kept through our lives,
And love, love will tear us apart again. *(x 2)*

# 1980 — Vienna

Words & Music by Midge Ure,
William Currie, Warren Cann &
Christopher Allen

© Copyright 1980 Mood Music Limited/Hot Food
Music Limited/Jump Jet Music Limited/Sing Sing
Songs Limited/PolyGram Music Publishing Limited.
Universal Music Publishing Limited.
All Rights Reserved. International Copyright Secured.

**Verse 2:**

The music is weaving,
Haunting notes, pizzicato strings; the rhythm is calling.
Alone in the night as the daylight brings a cool empty silence.
The warmth of your hand and a cold grey sky; it fades to the distance.
The image has gone, only you and I; it means nothing to me.
This means nothing to me. Oh, Vienna.

# 1981

# Ghost Town

Words & Music by Jerry Dammers
© Copyright 1981 Plangent Visions Music Limited.
All Rights Reserved. International Copyright Secured.

Spookily ♩ = 74

1. This town (town___) is 'come - in' like a ghost town.
(Verse 2 see block lyrics)

All the clubs___ are be - ing closed down._____ This place (town___) is 'come - in' like a ghost town.

Bands won't play no more. Too much fight - in' on the dance floor. La___ la la la la la___ la la la

la la la la la la la la la. La la_____ la la la la la la la.

Do you re - mem - ber the good old days___ be - fore the

ghost town? We danced and sang___ and the mu - sic played___ in our dear

boom town. This town___ is 'com - in' like a ghost town.

Verse 2:
This town is 'comin' like a ghost town,
Why must the youth fight against themself?
Goverment's leavin' the youths on the shelf,
This place is 'comin' like a ghost town.
No job to be found in this country,
Can't go on no more, the people gettin' angry.

La la la la *etc.*

# Golden Brown

Words & Music by Jean-Jacques Burnel, Jet Black, Hugh Cornwell & David Greenfield

© Copyright 1981 Plumbshaft Limited/Complete Music Limited (75%)/EMI Music Publishing Limited (25%). All Rights Reserved. International Copyright Secured.

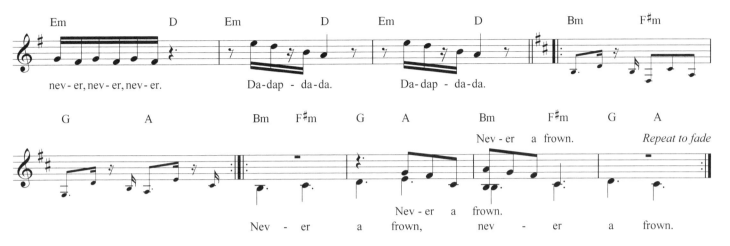

nev-er, nev-er, nev-er.  Da-dap - da-da.  Da-dap - da-da.

Nev - er a frown.  *Repeat to fade*

Nev - er a frown.

Nev - er a frown, nev - er a frown.

*Verse 2:*
Every time is just like the last,
On her ship, tied to the mast,
To distant lands, takes both my hands,
Never a frown, with Golden Brown.

*Verse 3:*
Golden Brown, finer temptress,
Through the ages, she's heading west,
From far away, stays for a day,
Never a frown, with Golden Brown.

The Stranglers, left to right, Jean-Jacques Burnel, Jet Black, Dave Greenfield and Hugh Cornwell.

# 1981

# In The Air Tonight

Words & Music by Phil Collins
© Copyright 1981 Effectsound Limited.
Hit & Run Music (Publishing) Limited.
All Rights Reserved. International Copyright Secured.

**Moderately**

1. I can feel it com - ing in the air to - night,___ oh Lord.___
*(Verses 2 & 3 see block lyrics)*

And I've been wait - ing for this mo - ment for all my life,___ oh Lord.___

Can you feel it com - ing in the air to - night,___ oh Lord,___ oh Lord.

Well, if

you told me___ you were drown - ing I would not lend___ a hand. I've

seen your face___ be - fore, my___ friend, but I don't know if you know___ who I am.___ Well,

I was there___ and I saw___ what you did, I saw it with my own two eyes.___ So you can

wipe off that grin. I know where you've been,___ it's all been a pack of lies.

Coda
I can feel it in the air to - night, oh Lord,___ oh Lord.___

And I've been wait-ing for this mo-ment for all my life,___ oh Lord.___

And I can feel it com - ing in the air to-night,___ oh Lord,___

well, I've been wait-ing for this mo-ment for all my life,___ oh Lord.___

*Verse 2:*
And I can feel it coming in the air tonight, oh Lord.
Well, I've been waiting for this moment for all my life, oh Lord.
I can feel it coming in the air tonight, oh Lord, oh Lord.
Well I remember, I remember, don't worry.
How could I ever forget, it's the first time,
The last time we ever met.
But I know the reason why you keep this silence up,
No you don't fool me.
The hurt doesn't show but the pain still grows,
It's no stranger to you or me.

*Verse 3:*
And I can feel it coming in the air tonight, oh Lord.
Well, I've been waiting for this moment for all my life, oh Lord.
*(Coda)*

Drummer Phil Collins assumed the vocalist's role in Genesis after the departure of Peter Gabriel, then went on to an extraordinary successful solo career.

# 1981     Memory

Music by Andrew Lloyd Webber
Text by Trevor Nunn after T.S. Eliot

Music © Copyright 1981 Andrew Lloyd Webber licensed
to The Really Useful Group Limited (50%).
Text © Copyright 1981 Trevor Nunn/Set Copyrights
Limited/Faber Music Limited (50%).
All Rights Reserved. International Copyright Secured.

leave   me____   all   a - lone with the   mem   -   'ry____   of   my days in the   sun.____   If   you

touch   me   you'll un - der - stand what   hap-pin-ness is.   Look   a   new   day   has   be - gun.

*Verse 2:*
Memory all alone in the moonlight.
I can smile at the old days, I was beautiful then.
I remember the time I knew what happiness was.
Let the memory live again.

*Verse 3:*
Daylight. I must wait for the sunrise,
I must think of a new life and I mustn't give in.
When the dawn comes tonight will be a memory too
And a new day will begin.

Memory all alone in the moonlight.
I can smile at the old days,
I was beautiful then.
I remember the time I knew what happiness was.
Let the memory live again.

Andrew Lloyd Webber premiered some settings of T. S. Eliot's poems from *Old Possum's Book Of Practical Cats* during the annual Sydmonton Festival (at his country estate in Berkshire) in 1980. Valerie Eliot, the poet's widow, was charmed by them, and handed Lloyd Webber a few precious but unpublished fragments of Eliot verse – including, most crucially, a poem about "Grizabella: the Glamour Cat." As Lloyd Webber recalls, "The musical and dramatic images that this created for me made me feel that

there was very much more to the project than I had realised." You can say that again! Working with Royal Shakespeare Company director Trevor Nunn and choreographer Gillian Lynne, and with a fledgling producer called Cameron Mackintosh, Lloyd Webber set about fashioning an entirely new kind of theatre presentation: a revolutionary dance musical, based on a book of poems about cats!

For Grizabella's big song, Lloyd Webber remembered the melody which he'd considered using

in *Evita* until 'Don't Cry For Me, Argentina' came along. He'd then tucked it away in his fabled bottom drawer for a possible future musical version of *Sunset Boulevard*.

However, it proved to be the perfect choice for *Cats*, with a lyric by Trevor Nunn based on images from Eliot's poems. Or, as the copyright line says (in classic RSC parlance): "Text by Trevor Nunn after T. S. Eliot."

Above, left to right, Bonnie Langford, Elaine Paige and Finola Hughes.

# Prince Charming

Words & Music by Adam Ant &
Marco Pirroni

© Copyright 1981 BMG Music Publishing Limited.
All Rights Reserved. International Copyright Secured.

Adam Ant applies his make up.

# 1981

# You Drive Me Crazy

Words & Music by Ronnie Harwood
© Copyright 1981 Campbell Connelly & Company Limited.
All Rights Reserved. International Copyright Secured.

**Verse 3:**
I love you baby and it's plain to see,
I love you honey, it was meant to be;
You drive me crazy,
You drive me crazy.

**Verse 5:**
And when I'm looking in those big blue eyes,
I started floating down in paradise;
You drive me crazy,
You drive me crazy.

# 1982

# Come On Eileen

Words & Music by Kevin Rowland,
James Paterson & Kevin Adams
© Copyright 1982 EMI Music Publishing Limited (80%)/
Kevin Adams Music Limited (20%).
All Rights Reserved. International Copyright Secured.

**Country feel** ♩ = 104

1. Poor old John-ny Ray___ sound-ed sad up - on___ the ra - di - o___ moved a mill-ion hearts in mo - no.

Our moth - ers cried,___ sang a - long, who'd blame_ them?

You've grown, *(you're grown up)* so grown, *(so grown up).* Now___ I must say more_ than ev - er. *(Come on_ Eil- een)*

Too - ra, too - ra, too - ra, loo - rye_ aye. And we can sing just like our fath - ers.___

Come on Eil - een,___ oh I swear,(what he means) at this mom -

- ent, you mean ev - 'ry thing._ You in that dress,_ my thoughts (I con - fess)_ verge on dir-

- ty. Ah come on___ Ei - leen._ *(banjo)*

2. These peo - ple round here___ wear beat - en

down eyes, sunk___ in smoke dried fa - ces they're re - signed to what their fate is. But

not us *(no nev - er.)* no not us *(no nev - er).* We___ are far too young and clev - er. *(Re - mem - ber)*

Kevin Rowland recently confessed the true inspiration for his song: not an ex-girlfriend called Eileen, but a Swedish television presenter! In 1981 Rowland was being interviewed for Swedish TV by a very attractive lady. While she asked him searching questions on the spiritual nature of Dexy's lyrics, all he could think about was how gorgeous she was! The story behind the song's success is fascinating, too. Rowland remembers: "The writing started as a collaborative process. Jim Paterson began by working out the chord structure and I tried various melodies over the top; our normal, tried and tested way of working. Until I became, shall we say, a little obsessed…" Rowland kept tinkering with the song in different keys until Paterson finally left the band in frustration. "Then the record label said they didn't want to release the song – it was actually a radio plugger who persuaded them it would make a great single. It crawled into the charts on the strength of a couple of radio plays a week and eventually made number thirty-three. Then in a huge turn of fortune it suddenly flew to number nine – and then to Number One, where it stayed for four weeks! It became the biggest-selling single of 1982 and even went to Number One in America. Not bad for a song that nearly split up the band, sent me to the verge of mania and then almost wasn't released!" It has also been adapted as a football song (see the note on 'Three Lions' for more on this topic), even though 'Come On England' doesn't scan quite as well as the original lyric…

# 1982 Mad World

Words & Music by Roland Orzabal
© Copyright 1982 Roland Orzabal Limited.
Chrysalis Music Limited.
All Rights Reserved. International Copyright Secured.

**Somberly** ♩ = 88

1. All a-round me are fa - mi-liar fa - ces, worn out pla - ces, worn out fa - ces.
*(Verse 2 see block lyrics)*

Bright and ear - ly for their dai - ly ra - ces, go-ing no - where, go-ing no - where.

Their tears are fill-ing up their glass - es, no ex - pres - sion, no ex - pres - sion.

Hide my head, I wan-na drown my sor - row, no to - mor - row, no to - mor - row.

And I find it kin-da fun - ny, I find it kin-da sad, that dreams in which I'm dy-ing are the best I've ev - er

had. I find it hard to tell you, I find it hard to take when peo-ple run in cir-cles it's a ver - y ver - y

mad world. Mad world.

En - larg - en your world. Mad world.

*Verse 2:*

Children waiting for the day they feel good,
Happy Birthday, Happy Birthday.
And I feel the way that ev'ry child should sit and listen, sit and listen.
Went to school and I was very nervous,
No one knew me, no one knew me.
Hello teacher, tell me what's my lesson,
Look right through me, look right through me.

# 1982     Rio

Words & Music by Simon Le Bon,
Nick Rhodes, John Taylor, Andy
Taylor & Roger Taylor
© Copyright 1982 Gloucester Place Music Limited.
All Rights Reserved. International Copyright Secured.

And I___ might find her if___ I'm look - ing like___ I can.

Oh Ri - o, Ri - o,___ hear them shout a - cross the land,___

from moun - tains in the North___ down to the Ri - o Grande.___

*Repeat to fade*

Doo,___ doo, doo,___ doo, doo, doo.　　Doo,___ doo, doo,___ doo, doo, doo.

*Verse 2:*
I've seen you on the beach and I've seen you on TV,
Two of a billion stars;
It means so much to me, like a birthday or a pretty view,
But then I'm sure that you know it's just for you.

*Verse 3:*
Hey now, wow, look at that. Did he nearly run you down?
At the end of the drive, the lawmen arrive,
You make me feel alive, alive, alive.
I'll take my chance, 'cause luck is on my side.
I tell you something, I know what you're thinking.
I tell you something, I know what you're thinking.

Named after the angel in the movie
Barbarella, Duran Duran epitomised
the New Romantic style that came
into fashion in the UK in the early
eighties. Singer Simon Le Bon's hobby
was yacht racing, and the pop world
was distraught when in 1985 he
almost drowned off the Cornish coast.

# 1982

# Thriller

Words & Music by Rod Temperton

**With a driving beat**  ♩ = 118

1. It's close to mid - night,___ and some - thin' ev - il's lurk - in' in the dark.___
*(Verses 2 & 3 see block lyrics)*

Un - der the moon - light___ you

see a sight that al - most stops your heart.___ You try to scream,___ but

ter - ror takes___ the sound___ be - fore___ you make___ it.___ You start to freeze___

as hor - ror looks___ you right___ be - tween___ the eyes.___ You're par - al - yzed.___

___ 'Cause this is thrill - er,___ thrill - er night, and no one's gon - na save___ you from the beast___
*(Choruses 2 & 3 see block lyrics)*

___ a - bout to strike. You know it's thrill - er,___ thrill - er night; you're fight ing for your life___ in - side a

**1.**

kill - er, thrill - er to - night.___

**2.**

kill - er, thrill - er to - night. Night creat - ures call and___ the dead start___ to walk in___ their

**To Coda** ⊕

mas - quer - ade.  There's__ no es - cap - in'__ the jaws of__ the a - lien__ this

time._____ This is__ the end of your life._____

*D.C. al Coda*

*Coda*

kill - er, dill - er, chill - er, thrill - er here to - night.__ 'Cause this is thrill - er,__

thrill - er night; girl, I can thrill you more_ than an - y ghost__ would ev - er dare_ try._ Thrill - er,__

thrill - er night; so let me hold you tight_ and share a kill - er, thrill - er.

I'm gon - na thrill you to - night.__

*Repeat ad lib. to end*

(Rap see block lyrics)

*Verse 2:*
You hear the door slam,
And realize there's nowhere left to run.
You feel the cold hand,
And wonder if you'll ever see the sun.
You close your eyes,
And hope that this is just imagination.
But all the while
You hear the creature creepin' up behind;
You're out of time.

*Chorus 2:*
'Cause this is thriller, thriller night;
There ain't no second chance,
Against the thing with forty eyes.
You know it's thriller, thriller night;
You're fighting for your life
Inside a killer thriller tonight.

*Verse 3:*
They're out to get you;
There's demons closin' in on every side.
They will posess you,
Unless you change that number on your dial.
Now is the time
For you and I to cuddle close together,
All through the night.
I'll save you from the terror on the screen;
I'll make you see.

*Chorus 3:*
That this is thriller, thriller night;
'Cause I could thrill you more
Than any ghost would dare to try.
Girl, this is thriller, thriller night,
So let me hold you tight
And share a killer, diller, chiller, thriller here tonight...

*Rap:*
Darkness falls across the land;
The midnight hour is close at hand.
Creatures crawl in search of blood,
To terrorize y'awl's neighbourhood.
And whosoever shall be found
Without the soul for getting down,
Must stand and face the hounds of hell,
And rot inside a corpse's shell.

The foulest stench is in the air,
The funk of forty thousand years;
And grizzly ghouls from every tomb
Are closing in to seal your doom,
And though you fight to stay alive,
Your body starts to shiver;
For no mere mortal can resist
The evil of a thriller.

# 1983 | Bird Of Paradise

Words & Music by Snowy White
© Copyright 1983 Campbell Connelly & Company Limited.
All Rights Reserved. International Copyright Secured.

*Soulfully*

1. Saw you fly- in' by, a flash of tur-quoise blue.__ I just had__ to try__ to keep your life__ with you.__

My bird of par - a- dise, sweet bird of par - a -dise.__

2. Wish that I could fly, *(Verse 3 see block lyrics)* I'd be bes-ide you now.__

But I could on - ly sigh__ and watch you cir-cle round.__

My bird of par - a- dise, sweet bird of par - a -dise.__

My bird of par - a- dise,___ sweet bird of par - a -dise,__

**1.** my bird of par - a- dise.___ 3. Saw you fly a -   **2.**

*Verse 3:*
Saw you fly away,
When will you come again?
So I can watch you play in the pouring rain.

# 1983

# Every Breath You Take

Words & Music by Sting
© Copyright 1983 Magnetic Publishing Limited/EMI
Music Publishing Limited.
All Rights Reserved. International Copyright Secured.

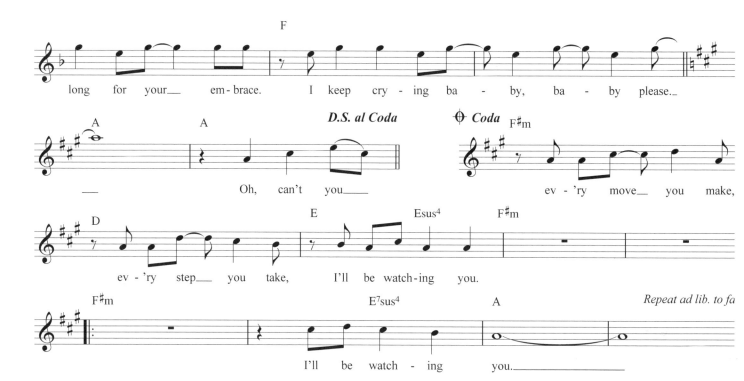

long for your___ em-brace. I keep cry-ing ba-by, ba-by please.___

*D.S. al Coda*   *Coda*

Oh, can't you___   ev-'ry move___ you make,

ev-'ry step___ you take, I'll be watch-ing you.

*Repeat ad lib. to fa*

I'll be watch-ing you._____

Like most songwriters, Sting is resigned to the vagaries of inspiration: "There have been times that I've written a melody and it's been with me for two years, until I've found the right idea to go with it. Or the right lyrics have sat around undressed – without music – for months, years at a time. So I'm quite patient with songwriting. You can't bully the muse." By contrast, however, 'Every Breath You Take' was written in about five minutes! "The power of the song for me is that it's ambivalent. It's both romantic, sentimental, and, on the other side, it's sinister and cruel. It's about surveillance and owning someone. But the reaction is one of seduction…"

It was the The Police's fifth chart-topper, staying at Number One in the UK for four weeks, and for even longer in the USA, where the song also won a Grammy Award.

The Police, left to right, Stuart Copeland, Sting and Andy Summers.

# 1983

# Here Comes The Rain Again

Words & Music by Annie Lennox &
David A Stewart

4. Here comes the rain___ a - gain,___ fall - ing on my head like a mem - o - ry,___

fall - ing on my head like new em - o - tion.

I want to walk in the op - en wind,___ I want to talk like lov - ers do,___

want to dive in - to your oc - ean, is it rain - ing___ with you?___

Verse 2:
Here comes the rain again,
Falling on my head like a tragedy,
Tearing me apart like a new emotion,
I want to breathe in the open wind,
I want to kiss like lovers do,
Want to dive into your ocean,
Is it raining with you.?

Verse 3:
Here comes the rain again,
Falling on my head like a memory,
Falling on my head like a new emotion,
I want to walk in the open wind,
I want to talk like lovers do,
Want to dive into your ocean,
Is it raining with you.

Here comes the **rain again,**
falling on my head like a memory.
Falling on my head like a new emotion.

# 1983 | Karma Chameleon

Words & Music by George O'Dowd, Jonathan Moss, Roy Hay, Michael Craig & Philip Pickett

Outrageously camp Boy George fronted Culture Club, and is now a very successful DJ.

*Verse 2:*
Didn't hear your wicked words every day.
And you used to be so sweet. I heard you say
That my love was an addiction.
When we cling, our love is strong.
When you go, you're gone forever,
You string along, you string along.

# 1983 True

Words & Music by Gary Kemp
© Copyright 1983 Reformation Publishing Company Limited.
All Rights Reserved. International Copyright Secured.

**With a Motown feel** ♩ = 98

Ha, ha, ha, ha,_____ ha._____

1. So true,____ fun-ny how it seems.____
*(Verse 2 see block lyrics)*

al-ways in time,____ but nev - er in line for dreams.____ Head o - ver heels____ when toe to toe,____

____ this is the sound____ of my soul,____ this is the sound.____

I bought a tick-et to the world,____ but now I've come back a - gain.____

Why do I find it hard__ to write the next__ line?____ When I want the truth to be said.____

Ha, ha, ha, ha,____ ha. I know this____

much is__ true.____ Ha, ha, ha, ha,____ ha.____ I know this____

*Verse 2:*
With a thrill in my head and a pill on my tongue,
Dissolve the nerves that have just begun.
Listening to Marvin all night long.
This is the sound of my soul, this is the sound.

Always slipping from my hands,
Sand's a time of its own.
Take your seaside arms and write the next line,
Oh, I want the truth to be known...
Ha, ha, ha, ha, ha. I know this much is true.
Ha, ha, ha, ha, ha. I know this much is true.

# 1984

# Careless Whisper

Words & Music by George Michael & Andrew Ridgeley

© Copyright 1984 Wham Music Limited (75%)/Morrison Leahy Music Limited (25%).
All Rights Reserved. International Copyright Secured.

**Slowly**

*Sax solo*

1. I feel so__ un - sure__ as I take your hand__ and lead you
*(Verses 2 & 3 see block lyrics)*

to the dance floor; as the mus-ic dies__ some-thing in your eyes__ calls to mind a sil-ver screen__ and

you're its sad good - bye.__ I'm nev-er gon-na dance a-gain;__ guil - ty feet have got__ no rhy-thm,

though it's ea - sy to pre-tend,__ I know you're not__ a fool.__ I should have known bet-ter than to cheat a friend,__ and

*To Coda* **1.**

waste a chance that I've__ been giv-en, so I'm nev-er gon-na dance a-gain__ the way I dance_with you.__

**2.** **D.S. al Coda** *(with repeat)* **Coda**

way I dance_ with you, oh.__ way I dance__ with you.__

*Sax solo*

---

**Verse 2:**
Time can never mend
The careless whisper of a good friend.
To the heart and mind,
Ignorance is kind.
There's no comfort in the truth,
Pain is all you'll find.

**Verse 3:**
Tonight the music seems so loud,
I wish that we could lose this crowd.
Maybe it's better this way,
If we'd hurt each other with the things we want to say.
We could have been so good together,
We could have lived this dance forever,
But now who's gonna dance with me? Please dance.

I'm never gonna dance again;
guilty feet have got no rhythm,
though it's easy to pretend,
I know you're not a fool.

I should've known better than to cheat a friend,
and waste the chance that I've been given,
so I'm never gonna dance again
the way I dance with you.

George Michael, above, had the inspiration for the tune of this song as he was boarding a bus and went upstairs to sit at the back and start putting words to it. He would subsequently win the Ivor Novello Award for songwriter of the year at the tender age of twenty-one. The title is buried pretty deep in the lyrics (which also reflect his day-job at the time, working in a cinema), but even so 'Careless Whisper' became an August 1984 charttopper almost immediately after Wham!'s first Number One, 'Wake Me Up Before You Go-Go', this was another chart-topper. It also marked George Michael's first solo outing as a performer, even though the song was co-written with his Wham! partner, Andrew Ridgeley. At the time Michael was still comfortable with Wham! and the duo was to have another Number One hit ('Freedom') later in 1984, not breaking up until 1986.

# 1984

# I Should Have Known Better

Words & Music by Jim Diamond & Graham Lyle

© Copyright 1984 Diamond Brothers Music/Goodsingle Limited.
Hornall Brothers Music Limited.

**Rock Ballad**

And I should have known bet-ter, to lie to one as beau-ti-ful as you.__ Yeah, I should have known bet-ter, to take a chance on ev-er los-ing you,__ but I thought you'd un-der-stand, can you for-give me? 1. I

*(Verse 2 see block lyric)*

saw you walk-ing by__ the oth-er day,__ I know that you__ saw me you turned a-way, and I__ was lost, you see, I've nev-er loved__ no-one as much as you; I've fooled a-round__ but tell me now__ just who is hurt-ing who?__ And I should have known bet-ter, to lie to one as beau-ti-ful as you.__ Yeah, I should have known bet-ter, to take a chance on ev-er los-

**To Coda ⊕**

-ing you,__ but I thought you'd un-der-stand, can you for-give me?

**Verse 2:**

It's true, I took our love for granted all along,
I'm trying to explain where I went wrong,
I just don't know,
I cry, the tears don't seem to help me carry on,
And now there is no chance you'll come back home,
Got too much pride.

I should have known better,
to **lie** to one as beautiful as you.

# The Power Of Love

Words & Music by Holly Johnson,
Mark O'Toole, Peter Gill & Brian
Nash

*I'll protect you from the hooded claw, keep the vampires from your door.*

*(Verse 2 see block lyrics)*

1. I,_____ feels like fire,_____ I'm so___ in love with you. Dreams are like an - gels, they keep bad at bay. (Bad at bay.__ )

Love is the light, scar - ing dark-ness a - way._____ I'm so___ in love with you, purge the soul. Make love your___ goal._____ The pow - er of love,__

__ a force from a - bove,_____ clean-ing my soul. Flame on, burn, de - sire,

**1.**
__ love with tongues of fire,_____ purge the soul. Make love your__ goal.

**2.**
Make love your__ goal._____

The power of love,
# a force from above, cleaning my soul.

'The Power Of Love' must be one of the most oversubscribed titles in popular music. No less than three songs of this title were originally released in late 1984 and 1985. The Frankie Goes To Hollywood 'The Power Of Love' was the third single taken from their album *Welcome*

*To The Pleasuredome* and song writing credits went to the whole band. With its innocuous spiritual overtones it reached Number One in the UK on 8 December 1984 with the help of a Godley & Creme-directed, nativity-flavoured video that Frankie frontman Holly Johnson described

as "naff". The song's chart success meant that FGTH equalled Gerry and the Pacemakers' run of having all first three singles make the Number One slot.

FGTH, in Hollywood, left to right, Paul Rutherford, Mark O'Toole, Peter Gill, Holly Johnson & Brian Nash.

This time   we go— sub-lime,_   lov-ers en-twined, div-ine,_ div-ine.   Love is dan - ger,   love is___ pleas-ure._

Love is pure,_   the on - ly treas-ure.   I'm   so in love with you,   purge the soul._

Make   love   your____   goal.____

The pow-er   of love,_____   a force from a-bove,_____   clean-ing my soul._

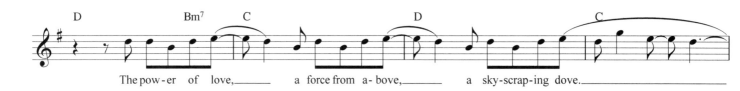

The pow-er   of love,_____   a force from a- bove,_____   a sky-scrap-ing dove._____

— Flame on, burn, de-sire,___   love,   with tongues of fire,___   purge the soul.   Make love   your___

*I'll protect you from the hooded claw,*
*keep the vampires from your door.*

*Verse 2:*
I'll protect you from the hooded claw,
Keep the vampires from you door.
When the chips are down I'll be around,
With my undying, death-defying love for you.
Envy will hurt itself,
Let yourself be beautiful.
Sparkling love, flowers and pearls and pretty girls,
Love is like an energy,
Rushing in, rushing inside of me, yeah.

# 1985

# EastEnders

Music by Leslie Osborne & Simon May

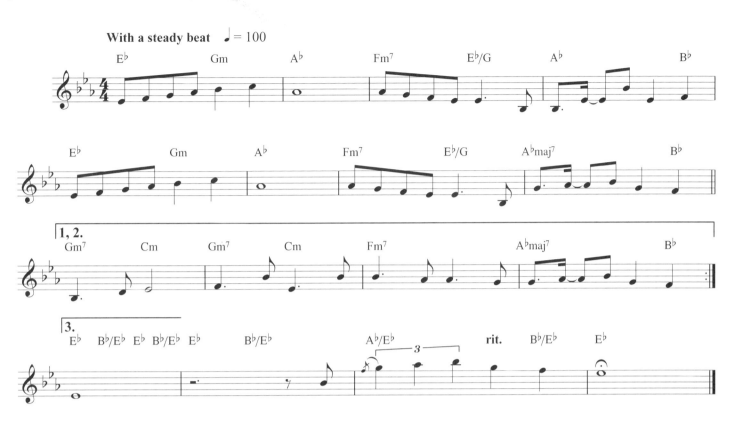

**Original BBC cast of Eastenders outside the Queen Vic in Albert Square E20**

Robert Smith

# 1985

# In Between Days

Words & Music by Robert Smith
© Copyright 1985 Fiction Songs Limited.
BMG Music Publishing Limited.
All Rights Reserved. International Copyright Secured.

**With a driving beat**  ♩ = 142

1. Yes - ter - day___ I got___ so old,___ I felt like I___ could die.___
*(Verse 2 see block lyrics)*

Yes - ter - day___ I got___ so old,___ it made me want to cry.___ Go on,___

___ go on,___ just walk___ a - way;___ go on,___ go on,___ your choice___ is made.___ Go on,___

___ go on,___ and dis - ap - pear;___ go on,___ go on,___ a - way___ from here.___ And I

know I was wrong when I said it was true,___ that it could-n't be me and be her___

___ in - be - tween___ with - out you, with - out___ you.

**1.**

The long, fluctuating career of The Cure (founded 1976 and still going with various personnel changes) saw them as the standard bearers of alternative rock during the eighties. In 1985 the band released the album The Head On The Door from which the song 'In Between Days' was taken. Lyrically rather undistinguished, it nonetheless achieved the usual Cure effect of creating its mood through the texture of the recording rather than the bones of the song. Led by Goth-pop poster boy Robert Smith, of the panda bear make-up and birds nest hair, The Cure has become one of the most successful and influential outfits of the past four decades, with the type of devoted following that puts the fan into fanatical.

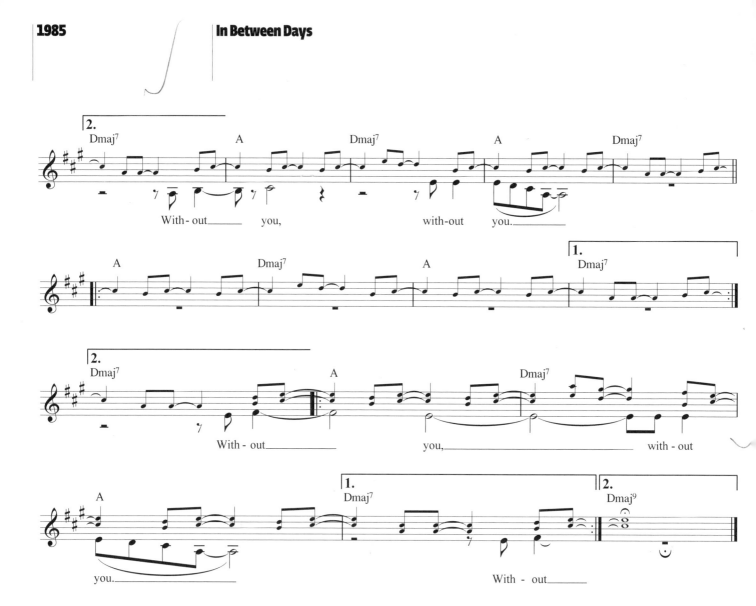

*Verse 2:*
Yesterday I got so scared, I shivered like a child.
Yesterday away from you, it froze me deep inside.
Come back, come back, don't walk away; come back, come back, come back today.
Come back, come back, why can't you see? Come back, come back, come back to me.

And I know I was wrong when I said it was true,
That it couldn't be me and be her inbetween without you, without you.

Yesterday I got so old,
I felt like I could die.
Yesterday I got so old,
It made me want to cry.

# 1985

# Wonderful Life

Words & Music by Colin Vearncombe
© Copyright 1985 Hornall Brothers Music Limited.
All Rights Reserved. International Copyright Secured.

***D.S. al Coda***  $\oplus$ ***Coda***

G — D/F#  D  Em

life.     No need  to   run_____     and

G        Em       Am      D           Em

hide,   it's  a  won-der-ful, won-der-ful  life.    No need  to   run_____     and_____

G        Em       Am      D           Em

cry,    it's  a  won-der-ful, won-der-ful  life._____

Em⁹      Em                      Em⁹        Em

Won - der - ful  life.                    It's a won-der- ful_____ life.

*Verse 2:*
The sun's in your eyes, the heat is in your hair,
They seem to hate you because you're there.
And I need a friend, oh, I need a friend
To make me happy, not stand here on my own.

Colin Vearncombe was the leader
of Black, a punk trio from Liverpool,
who reached number eight with
'Wonderful Life' in 1987.

No need to **run**
and **hide,**
it's a wonderful,
wonderful life.

# 1986 The Lady In Red

Words & Music by Chris de Burgh
© Copyright 1986 Rondor Music (London) Limited.
All Rights Reserved. International Copyright Secured.

*Verse 2:*

I've never seen you looking so gorgeous as you did tonight.

I've never seen you shine so bright,

You were amazing.

I've never seen so many people want to be there by your side,

And when you turned to me and smiled, it took my breath away,

I have never had such a feeling,

Such a feeling of complete and utter love,

As I do tonight.

# There Is A Light That Never Goes Out

Words & Music by Morrissey & Johnny Marr

© Copyright 1986 Chrysalis Music Limited (50%)/Marr Songs Limited/Universal Music Publishing Limited (50%).
All Rights Reserved. International Copyright Secured.

**Lively** ♩ = 135

1. Take me out to-night, where there's
(Verse 3 see block lyrics)

mus-ic and there's peop-le and they're young and a-live. And driv-

-ing in your car, I nev-er, nev-er want to go home. Bec-ause I have-n't

got one, an-y-more.

2. Take me out to-night, be-cause I
(Verse 4 see block lyrics)

want to see peop-le and I want to see life. And driv-

-ing in your car, oh, please don't drop me home. Be-cause it's not

my home, it's their home and I'm wel-come no more.

*Verse 3:*
Take me out tonight,
Take me anywhere, I don't care,
I don't care, I don't care,
And in the darkened underpass,
I thought, oh God,
My chance has come at last,
But then a strange fear gripped me and I just couldn't ask.

*Verse 4:*
Take me out tonight,
Oh, take me anywhere, I don't care,
I don't care, I don't care,
And driving in your car,
I never, never want to go home,
Because I haven't got one, la-di-da,
No, I haven't got one.

 Steven Morrissey and Johnny Marr were the leading lights in The Smiths, the best-loved indie band of the eighties.

I never, never want to go home.
Because I haven't got one, any more.

# Fairytale Of New York

Words & Music by Shane
MacGowan & Jem Finer

*Verse 2:*
Got on a lucky one; came in eighteen to one.
I've got a feeling this year's for me and you.
So happy Christmas, I love you baby;
I can see a better time when all our dreams come true.

*Verse 5:*
You're a bum. You're a punk. You're an old slut on junk,
Lying there almost dead on a drip in that bed.
You scum-bag, you maggot, you cheap lousy faggot.
Happy Christmas, you arse, I pray God it's our last.

You were handsome.
You were pretty,
Queen of New York City.
When the band finished playing,

# they howled out for more.

Written by Shane MacGowan and Jem Finer, this song is widely considered to be not only The Pogues' finest moment but also the greatest Christmas song of all time. A blend of two separate melodies, it was a long time in the composing but, when complete, this atmospheric tale of expatriate love and broken dreams was little short of magnificent. Featuring two Irish immigrants bickering at Christmas in New York City, it was eventually recorded as a duet between Shane MacGowan and Kirsty MacColl, MacColl having made a vocal guide for the female part at the request of her husband, the group's producer Steve Lillywhite. Its salty lyrics made it a tricky song for TV and radio to play, and it was darkly rumoured that the record only missed being Number One because the BBC, committed to airing the top song on *Top Of The Pops*, preferred that the Pet Shop Boys' *Always On My Mind* should be Number One. We shall never know.

# 1987

# It's A Sin

Words & Music by Neil Tennant & Chris Lowe

© Copyright 1987 Cage Music Limited.
Sony/ATV Music Publishing (UK) Limited.
All Rights Reserved. International Copyright Secured.

**With energy** ♩ = 130

1. When I look back up-on___ my life,___ it's al-ways
*(Verses 2 & 3 see block lyrics)*

with a sense_ of shame,___ I've al-ways been the one___ to___ blame.

For ev-'ry-thing I___ long___ to do,

___ no mat-ter when or where or___ who,___ has one thing in com-mon too:___

It's a, it's a, it's a,___ it's a sin,

it's a sin. Ev-'ry-thing I've ev-er done,

ev-'ry-thing I ev-er do, ev-'ry place_ I've ev-er been, ev-'ry-where I'm go-ing___ to:___

**1.** it's_ a___ sin.

**2.** it's_ a___ sin. Fath-er for-give___ me,

I tried not to do it. Turned ov-er a new___ leaf,

Cm
then__ tore__ right through it.

Cm/B♭

Cm
What-ev-er you taught__ me,

E♭m
I did-n't bel-ieve____ it,

Gm
fath-er you fought__ me,   'cause I

A♭
did-n't care___ and I

B♭
still don't

G
un-der-stand.___

*D.C. al Coda*

Coda (G)
It's__ a___ sin.

Cm    Fm    B♭    E♭    A♭

Fm    G
It's a,    it's a,    it's a,_____    it's a sin.

*Verse 2:*
At school they taught me how to be,
So pure in thought and word and deed,
They didn't quite succeed.

*Verse 3:*
So I look back upon my life,
Forever with a sense of shame,
I've always been the one to blame.

So I look back upon my life,

forever with a sense of shame,
I've always been the one to blame.

# 1987

# Never Gonna Give You Up

Words & Music by Mike Stock, Matt
Aitken & Pete Waterman
© Copyright 1987 Sids Songs Limited/Universal Music
Publishing Limited (33.34%)/All Boys Music Limited
(33.33%)/Mike Stock Publishing Limited (33.33%).
All Rights Reserved. International Copyright Secured.

*Fine*

tell a lie_____ and hurt___ you. Oo,_____ give you__ up. Oo,___

*Backing vocals continue*

_____ give you__ up. Nev - er gon - na give, nev - er gon - na give...

*D.C. al Fine*
*(without repeat)*

give you__ up. Nev - er gon - na give, nev - er gon - na give... give you__ up.

*Verses 2 & 3:*
We've known each other for so long.
Your heart's been aching, but your too shy to say it.
Inside we both know what's been going on;
We know the game and we're gonna play it.
And if you ask me how I'm feeling,
Don't tell me you're too blind to see.

Never gonna give you up,...*etc.*

Rick Astley became the nearly man of British pop in the mid-eighties. Taken under the wing of producers Stock, Aitken and Waterman, the boy with the soul-flavoured voice had been given a crash course in the
business and his first single was the obscure 'When You Gonna', which was credited to Rick & Lisa. His first fully-fledged solo outing was the uptempo 'Never Gonna Give You Up'
(written by Stock, Aitken and Waterman) which spent five weeks at the top of the British charts and became 1987's highest selling single. In January of the following year the song also topped the US singles chart and Astley enjoyed several other international hits before splitting with Stock, Aitken and Waterman, and largely withdrawing
from showbusiness for personal reasons.
Writers Pete Waterman, left, Matt Aitken, centre, and Mike Stock.

# 1988    Perfect

Words & Music by Mark E. Nevin
© Copyright 1988 MCA Music Limited.
Universal/MCA Music Limited.
All Rights Reserved. International Copyright Secured.

With a bounce ♩ = 136

1. I don't mind___ half-heart-ed love af-fairs.___

*(Verses 2 & 3 see block lyrics)*

I need___ some-one___ who___ real-ly cares.___ Life___ is too___

— short___ to play sil-ly games,___ I've prom-ised my-self___

I won't do___ that a-gain. It's___ got to be___ per-

fect.___ It's___ got to be___ worth it,___ yeah.___

Too___ ma-ny peo-ple take sec-ond best,___ well I won't take a-ny-thing less,___

— it's got to be,___ yeah,___ per - -

**1, 2.** - fect. **3.** -fect. It's got___ to be,___ yeah,___ worth___

it. It's got___ to be___ per - - fect.

*Verses 2 & 3:*
Young hearts are foolish, they make such mistakes;
They're much too eager to give their love away.
Well I have been foolish too many times,
Now I'm determined I'm gonna get it right.

Glasgow born Eddi Reader had done session and live work with Eurythmics and Alison Moyet before she teamed up with Mark Nevin to form Fairground Attraction in 1985.

# There She Goes

Words & Music by Lee Mavers
© Copyright 1988 Go! Discs Music.
Universal/Island Music Limited.
All Rights Reserved. International Copyright Secured.

**Moderately**

1. There she goes,___ there she goes___ a-gain,
*(Verses 2 & 4 see block lyrics)*

rac-ing thru' my____ brain.____ And I___ just___ can't__ con-tain_____ this

feel - in'____ that re-mains._____ 3. There she goes,___

___ there she goes___ a-gain.____ She calls my name, pulls my

train and no___ one___ else can feel my___ pain.___ But I___ just___ can't__ con-tain___

___ this feel - in' that re-mains._____ (Call___ my

There she goes___ There she goes.___
*name,* *call___ my* *name.* *There she goes___ a - gain.___*

___ There she goes.___
*There she goes___ a - gain.___* *There she goes___ a - gain.*

**Verse 2:**
There she blows,
There she blows again,
Pulsing thru' my vein.
And I just can't contain
This feelin' that remains.

**Verse 4:**
There she goes,
There she goes again,
Chasing down my lane.
And I just can't contain
This feelin' that remains.

# 1990

# A Little Time

Words & Music by Paul Heaton &
David Rotheray

Verse 2:
(*Male*)
I need a little room to find myself,
I need a little space to work it out,
I need a little room all alone,
I need a little...

(*Female*)
You need a little room for your big head,
Don't you, don't you?
You need a little space for a thousand beds,
Won't you, won't you?
Lips that promise, fear the worst,
Tongue so sharp the bubble burst...
Just into unjust.

Verse 3:
(*Male*)
I've had a little time to find the truth,
I've had a little room to check what's wrong,
I've had a little time and I still love you,
I've had a little...

(*Female*)
You had a little time and you had a little fun,
Didn't you, didn't you?
When you had yours do you think I had none,
Do you, do you?
The freedom that you wanted back
Is yours for good, I hope you're glad,
Sad into un-sad.

I had a little time to think it over *etc*.

'A Little Time', written by Paul Heaton and David Rotheray, featured a duet between The Beautiful South's Briana Corrigan and Dave Hemingway, and gave the group their first and only Number One single. Corrigan would later be recruited as a full-time member of the band where she would help to stage the little domestic dramas that Paul Heaton's songs often evoked. She was replaced by Jacqui Abbott in 1994. 'A Little Time' had a memorable video in which Corrigan and Hemingway were seen covered in flour in a kitchen that bore the signs of a frank exchange of views between a couple who were clearly not seeing eye to eye.
Left to right, Paul Heaton, Briana Corrigan and Dave Hemingway

# 1991    One

Words by Bono. Music by U2

© Copyright 1991 Blue Mountain Music Limited (for
the UK)/Mother Music (for the Republic of Ireland)/
PolyGram International Music Publishing Limited (for
the rest of the World).
All Rights Reserved. International Copyright Secured.

**Steadily** ♩ = 90

1. Is it get-ting bet - ter,____ or do you feel_ the same?_
*(Verses 2 & 3 see block lyrics)*

Will it make it eas - i - er on__ you,__ now____ you got__ some-one__ to blame?_

You__ say one love,_ one life__ when it's one need____

in the night. One love,_ we get_ to share_ it,_ leaves_ you ba - by if you

**1, 2.**

don't care____ for it.____

**3.**

__ Love__ is a tem - ple, love____ a high-er law,_ love_____ is a tem - ple, love__

__ the high-er law._ You ask__ me__ to en - ter__ but then you make me crawl, and

I can't__ be hold - ing on_____ to what_ you've got, when all_you've got_ is hurt.___

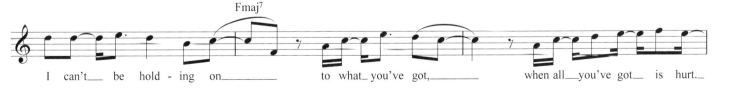

Hard work and an unshakeable belief in their own vision made U2 the biggest band in the world by the end of the eighties. Here Bono adopts a typically melodramatic pose while Edge turns on the guitar.

C      Am      Fmaj[7]      C

__ One love,__     one blood,__     one life__ you've got to   do what you should.__

Am      Fmaj[7]      C

One life,__    with each oth - er:    sis- ters,_____    broth - ers.__

Am      Fmaj[7]

One life_____ but we're   not the same,__ we get to   car - ry__ each oth - er,   car - ry__

C      C      Am      Fmaj[7]      C

__each oth - er.   One,_____     one.__

Am   Fmaj[7]    C      C      Am      Fmaj[7]      C

Ah,   ah.__      Oh,   ah,____   ah.____    Yeah.

*Verse 2:*

Did I disappoint you,
Or leave a bad taste in your mouth?
You act like you never had love,
And you want me to go without.
Well it's too late, tonight,
To drag the past out into the light.
We're one, but we're not the same,
We get to carry each other, carry each other...one.

*Verse 3:*

Have you come here for forgiveness?
Have you come to raise the dead?
Have you come here to play Jesus,
To the lepers in your head?
Did I ask too much, more than a lot?
You gave me nothing now it's all I got,
We're one, but we're not the same,
Well, we hurt each other, then we do it again. You say...

We're one, but we're not the same,
well, we hurt each other, **then we do it again.**

# Tears In Heaven

Words & Music by Eric Clapton &
Will Jennings

© Copyright 1991, 1995 & 2004 E.C. Music Limited
(87.5%)/Rondor Music (London) Limited (12.5%).
All Rights Reserved. International Copyright Secured.

Verse 2:
Would you hold my hand if I saw you in heaven?
Would you help me stand if I saw you in heaven?
I'll find my way through night and day
'Cause I know I just can't stay here in heaven.

Verse 3:
*Instrumental solo for first 8 bars*

Beyond the door there's peace, I'm sure
And I know there'll be no more tears in heaven.

Considered one of the greatest and most influential guitarists in popular music history, Eric Clapton, above, is more usually associated with interpreting the blues in a variety of musical settings than with confessional self-penned songs. He co-wrote 'Tears In Heaven' with Texas songwriter Will Jennings, and it was a ballad reflecting the anguish Clapton felt when his young son Conor fell to his death from a 53rd storey window of a New York condominium. The song was also featured in the movie *Rush* and Jennings won a Golden Globe for the lyrics.

I'll find my way through night and day, 'cause I know I just can't stay here in heaven.

# 1992 | Creep

Words & Music by Thom Yorke,
Jonny Greenwood, Colin Greenwood,
Ed O'Brien, Phil Selway, Albert
Hammond & Mike Hazlewood

*(Verse 2 see block lyrics)*

1. When you were here before, couldn't look you in the eye. You're just like an angel, your skin makes me cry. You float like a feather in a beautiful world. I wish I was special, you're so fucking special. But I'm a creep, I'm a weirdo. What the hell am I doing here? I don't belong here. (Oh)

1. I don't care if it hurts, oh. She's running out the door, she's running, she run, run, run, run. Whatever makes you hap-

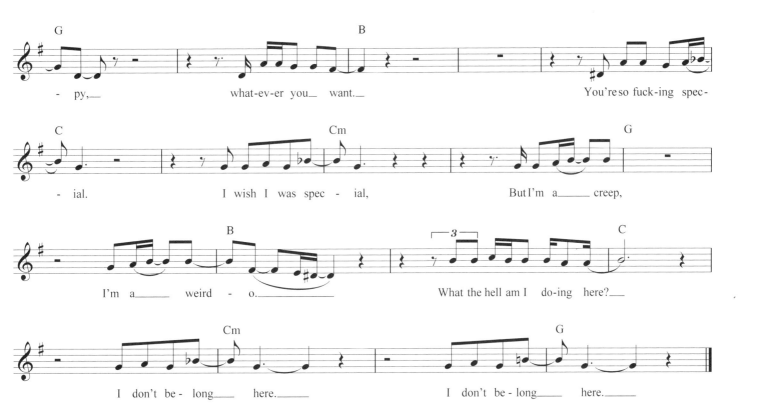

- py,— what-ev-er you— want.— You're so fuck-ing spec-

- ial. I wish I was spec - ial, But I'm a___ creep,

I'm a___ weird - o.___ What the hell am I do-ing here?—

I don't be - long__ here.___ I don't be - long__ here.___

*Verse 2:*

I don't care if it hurts,
I want to have control,
I want to have a perfect body,
I want a perfect soul,
I want you to notice,
When I'm not around,
You're so fucking special,
I wish I was special.

Radiohead's second single became a huge hit on its re-release, even though initially it had been taken off Radio 1's playlist after just two airings. It was issued in several different versions, partly because of one word in the lyric which caused offence in some territories overseas. (Can you guess which word?) After a while, the band tired of the song's renown and a later song, 'My Iron Lung,' refers to their love-hate relationship with it as the band's life-support system. Publishing note: The writing credits include not only the five members of Radiohead, but also veteran songwriters Albert Hammond and Mike Hazlewood. This was because certain elements of 'Creep' may bear a similarity to Hammond and Hazelwood's 1974 song for The Hollies, 'The Air That I Breathe'. Many pop songs carry within them the DNA of previous works. Such musical or lyrical recycling is often accidental or unconscious. However, sometimes an earlier song acts as an inspiration, providing a riff or a rhythm as a starting point for a new creation. At the other end of the scale, entire chunks of recordings are sampled. And there are many degrees in between. On this occasion, whether the inspiration was unconscious or intentional, acknowledgment was duly made to the writers of the earlier work. Left, Radiohead's Thom Yorke.

# 1994

# Girls And Boys

Words & Music by Damon Albarn,
Graham Coxon, Alex James & David
Rowntree

**With attitude!**

1. Street's like a jun - gle,_____ so call the pol - ice.
*(Verse 2 see block lyrics)*

Fol - low - ing the herd down to Greece,_ on ho - li - day.

Love in the nine - ties_____ is pa - ra - noid._

On sun - ny beach - es_____ take your chan - ces. Look - ing for:

Girls who are boys,_ who like boys_ to be girls,_ who do boys_ like they're girls,_ who do girls_ like they're boys._

Al - ways should_ be some - one you real - ly love._____

Girls who are boys,_ who like boys_ to be girls,_ who do boys_ like they're girls,_ who do girls_ like they're boys._

Al - ways should_ be some - one you real - ly love._____

Oh, oh, oh, oh, oh,_____ oh. Oh, oh oh, oh, oh._____

F5 — Eb5

Look - ing    for

G5 — C5

Girls who are boys,_ who like boys_ to be girls,_ who do boys_ like they're girls, who do girls_ like they're boys._

F5 — Eb5

Al - ways should_ be some - one you real - ly love._____

G5 — C5

Oh,  oh,  oh,  oh,  oh,____ oh.         Oh,  oh  oh,  oh,  oh.____

*Repeat to fade*

F5 — Eb5

*Verse 2:*
Avoiding all work, 'cause there's none available.
Like battery thinkers, count your thoughts on one two three four fingers.
Nothing is wasted, only reproduced.
You get nasty blisters.
Du bist sehr schön, but we haven't been introduced.

Always should be someone you really love.

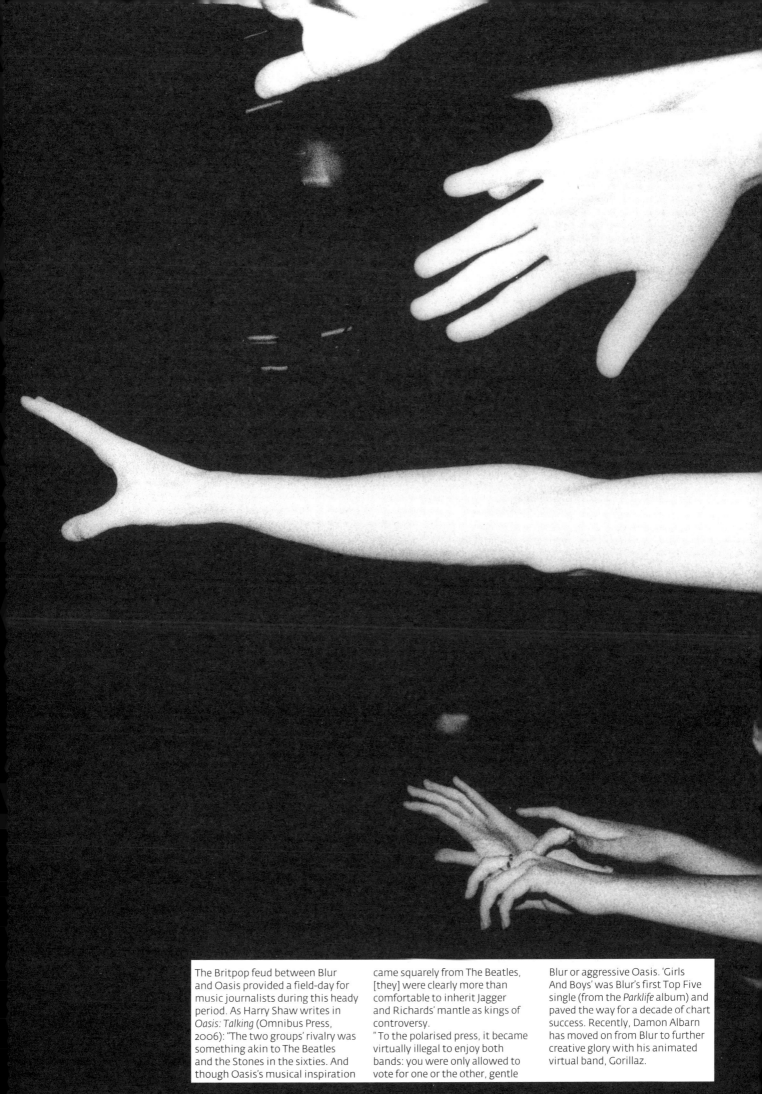

The Britpop feud between Blur and Oasis provided a field-day for music journalists during this heady period. As Harry Shaw writes in *Oasis: Talking* (Omnibus Press, 2006): "The two groups' rivalry was something akin to The Beatles and the Stones in the sixties. And though Oasis's musical inspiration came squarely from The Beatles, [they] were clearly more than comfortable to inherit Jagger and Richards' mantle as kings of controversy." To the polarised press, it became virtually illegal to enjoy both bands: you were only allowed to vote for one or the other, gentle Blur or aggressive Oasis. 'Girls And Boys' was Blur's first Top Five single (from the *Parklife* album) and paved the way for a decade of chart success. Recently, Damon Albarn has moved on from Blur to further creative glory with his animated virtual band, Gorillaz.

# 1995 | Alright

Words & Music by Gareth Coombes,
Daniel Goffey & Michael Quinn

*Verse 2:*

But we are young, we get by
Can't go mad, ain't got time
Sleep around, if we like
But we're alright.

*Verse 3:*

Got some cash, bought some wheels
Took it out 'cross the fields
Lost control, hit a wall
But we're alright.

Supergrass, left to right, Danny Goffey, Gaz Coombes & Mick Quinn

# 1995

# Back For Good

Words & Music by Gary Barlow
© Copyright 1995 EMI Virgin Music Limited.
All Rights Reserved. International Copyright Secured.

never be un-cov-ered a-gain.___ What - ev-er I said, what-ev-er I did__ I did-n't
mean it___ I just want you__ back for good.__
*(Want you back,    want you back.)*
*(Want you back for good.)*__   When-
-ev - er I'm wrong just tell me the song and I'll sing__ it.__ You'll be right and__ un-der-stood.__   I
*(Want you back,    want you back.)*

**1.** want you back__ for good.__

**2.** What - want you back__ for good.__   Oh,__ yeah.__

I guess now it's time,__ that you came back___ for good.

*Verse 2:*
Unaware but underlined,
I figured out the story,
It wasn't good,
But in a corner of my mind,
I celebrated glory,
But that was not to be,
In the twist of separation, you excelled at being free,
Can you find a little room inside for me?

Got a fist of pure emotion,
# got a head of shattered dreams.
Got to leave it,
got to leave it all behind now.

# 1995 Common People

Words by Jarvis Cocker
Music by Jarvis Cocker, Nick Banks,
Russell Senior, Candida Doyle &
Stephen Mackey

**Moderately**

1. She came from Greece she had a thirst for know-ledge,___ she stud-ied sculp-ture at Saint
*(Verse 2 see block lyrics)*

Mar-tin's Col-lege, that's where I___ caught her eye.___

She told me that her dad was load - ed, I said "In that case I'll have rum and

Co- ca Co- la." She said "Fine!"___ And then in thir-ty sec-onds time

___ she said; Chorus 1. "I want to live like com-mon peo - ple, I want to do what-
*(Chorus 2 see block lyrics)*

-ev - er com-mon peo-ple do.___ Want to sleep with com-mon peo - ple, I want to sleep with

**1.**

com-mon peo - ple like you.___ What else could I do?"___ I said

**2.**

"I'll see what I can do." ___ She just

smiled and held___ my hand.___ Rent a flat a-bove___ a shop,
*(Guitar solo 2nd time)*

___ cut your hair___ and get a job,___ smoke some fags___ and play___ some pool,___

I said pretend you've got no money,
She just laughed and said, "oh you're so funny."

I said "yeah? well I can't see anyone else smiling in here".

Jarvis Cocker's musical reprise of his relationship with a slumming little rich girl at Saint Martin's College of Art & Design was a great crowd pleaser and became Pulp's most successful single. From its quiet opening to its teeth-rattling crescendo 'Common People' is a truly original song, shot through with Cocker's mordant wit and lugubrious personality. The accompanying video featured an appearance from actress Sadie Frost as well as a decidedly underrehearsed dance routine devised by Cocker, above, himself.

_pre-tend you nev - er went_ to school.___ But still you'll nev - er get_ it right,

_'cos when you're laid_ in bed_ at night_ watch-ing roach - es climb_ the wall,_

_if you called_ your dad_ he could stop_ it all,_ yeah! Chorus 3. You'll nev - er live like
_(Chorus 4 see block lyrics)_

com-mon peo-ple,_ you'll nev - er do what - ev - er com-mon peo-ple do,_ nev - er fail like

com-mon peo - ple,_ you'll nev - er watch your life_ slide out of view,_____ and dance_

_and drink_ and screw,_ be-cause there's noth- ing else_ to do._____

_Play 6 times_

Want to live with com-mon peo - ple like you,_ want to live with

com-mon peo - ple like you._____ La_ la la_ la, Oh!_____ La

_la la_ la, Ooh!_____ La_ la la la la, oh you!

_Verse 2:_

I took her down to a supermarket,
I don't know why, but I had to start it somewhere,
So it started there.
I said "Pretend you've got no money,"
But she just laughed and said "Oh you're so funny!"
I said "Yeah?" _(Spoken)_ "Well, I can't see anyone else smiling in here."

_Chorus 2:_

"Are you sure you want to live like common people?"
You want to see whatever common people see,
Want to sleep with common people,
You want to sleep with common people like me.
But she didn't understand.
She just smiled and held my hand.

_Chorus 4:_

Sing along with the common people,
Sing along and it might just get you through,
Laugh along with the common people,
Laugh along even though they're laughing at you,
And the stupid things that you do,
Because you think that poor is cool.

# Don't Look Back In Anger

Words & Music by Noel Gallagher
© Copyright 1995 Creation Songs Limited/Oasis Music.
Sony/ATV Music Publishing (UK) Limited.
All Rights Reserved. International Copyright Secured.

Noel (left) and Liam Gallagher of Oasis

So Sally can wait\_\_ she knows it's too late\_\_ as we're walk - ing on by.\_

Her soul slides a - way,\_\_ but don't\_\_ look back\_

\_ in an - ger, don't look back in an - ger,\_\_\_\_ I heard you say,\_

at least not to - day.

*Verse 2:*

Take me to the place where you go,
Where nobody knows if it's night or day.
Please don't put your life in the hands,
Of a rock 'n' roll band who'll throw it all away.

I'm gonna start a revolution from my bed,
'Cause you said the brains I had went to my head.
Step outside 'cause summer time's in bloom.
Stand up beside the fireplace,
Take that look from off your face,
You ain't ever gonna burn my heart out.

Please don't put your life in the hands of a rock 'n' roll band,

# who'll throw it all away.

Anger is a particularly apt theme for an Oasis song, as the Gallagher brothers have gained notoriety for their intemperate pronouncements on other bands and musicians (except Paul Weller), life in general, and frequently even each other. During the Britpop saga, Noel allegedly turned down an Ivor Novello award when told that he would have to share it with Damon Albarn of Blur (see page 314). However, he wrote some scorching songs and nobody gets brownie points in this business for being all nice and fluffy, do they? The first two Oasis albums, *Definitely Maybe* and *(What's The Story) Morning Glory?*, went straight to the top of the charts and as Noel famously pointed out – with incontrovertible logic on his side – "There are ten bands in the Top Ten, five in the Top Five, but there's only one at Number One!"

# 1996

# A Design For Life

Words by Nicky Wire
Music by James Dean Bradfield,
Nicky Wire & Sean Moore
© Copyright 1996 Sony/ATV Music Publishing (UK) Limited.
All Rights Reserved. International Copyright Secured.

Steadily ♩. = 90

1. Lib - ra - ries gave us pow - er, then work came and made us free,

what price now for a shal - low piece of dig - ni -

- ty.  2. I wish I had a bot - tle, right here in my dirt - y
(Verse 3 see block lyrics)

face.  To wear the scars to show from where I

came.  We don't talk a - bout love, we on - ly wan - na

get drunk, and we are not al - lowed to spend, as

we are told that this is the end.  A de - sign

for life, a de - sign for life,

To Coda

a de - sign for life, a des - ign for life.  3. I

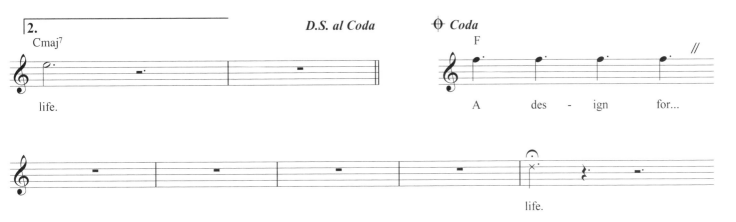

Verse 3:
I wish I had a battle, right here in my pretty face,
To wear the scars to show from where I came.
We don't talk about love,
We only wanna get drunk
And we are not allowed to spend,
As we are told that this is the end.

# Libraries gave us power,
# then work came and made us free,
## what price now for a shallow piece of dignity.

The Manic Street Preachers, left to right, James Dean Bradfield, Nicky Wire and Sean Moore, brought a lot of cultural and political baggage to this song. Its title echoed the Joy Division EP record 'An Ideal For Living' while the opening line "Libraries gave us power" was, rather more obscurely, a reference to an inscription above the entrance to the public library in the band's Welsh home town.

More worryingly the line "then work came and made us free" connotes the slogan Arbeit Macht Frei that adorned the gates of Nazi concentration camps. The Manics, Socialists to a man, grew up during the eighties miners' strikes and once dedicated an award to Arthur Scargill. In another display of commitment to Old Labour, they even played a gig in Cuba.

Words & Music by Matt Rowe,
Richard Stannard, Melanie Brown,
Victoria Adams, Geri Halliwell,
Emma Bunton & Melanie Chisholm

© Copyright 1996 Universal Music Publishing Limited
(50%)/EMI Music Publishing (WP) Limited (50%).
All Rights Reserved. International Copyright Secured.

# 1996

# 2 Become 1

had a lit-tle love____ now I'm back for more.
*Wan-na make love to ya ba-by.* I

need some love like I nev-er need-ed love be-fore.____
*Wan-na make love to ya ba-by.* I

had a lit-tle love__ now I'm back for more.
*Wan-na make love to ya ba-by.* Set your spir-it free_ it's the

**1, 2.**

**3.**

on - ly way_ to be._____ It's the

*Verse 2:*

Silly games that you were playing, empty words we both were saying,

Let's work it out boy, let's work it out boy.

Once again if we endeavour, love will bring us back together.

Take it or leave it, take it or leave it,

Are you as good as I remember baby?

Get it on, get it on, 'cause tonight is the night when two become one.

Riding on the crest of Girl Power, The Spice Girls swept all before them in the mid-nineties but never really recovered from the departure of Geri Halliwell, left to right Sporty (Melanie Chisholm), Baby (Emma Bunton), Posh (Victoria Adams, now Beckham), Scary (Melanie Brown) and Ginger (Geri).

# 1996 Three Lions

Words by David Baddiel & Frank Skinner.
Music by Ian Broudie
© Copyright 1996 Avalon Management Group Limited/
Chrysalis Music Limited.
All Rights Reserved. International Copyright Secured.

Boldly ♩ = 126

It's com-ing home,__ it's com-ing home,_ it's com-ing, foot-ball's com-ing home,__ it's com-ing home.__ It's com-ing home,_ it's com-ing, foot-ball's com-ing home,_ it's com-ing home.__

**1.** __ it's com-ing home.__ **2.** 1. Ev -'ry-one seems to know the score,_
*(Verse 2 see block lyrics)*

the'-ve seen it all__ be - fore,_____ they just know,_ they're so sure_ that Eng-land's going to throw it a-way,_ gon-na blow_ it a-way,_ but I know_ they can play.__ 'Cause I re-mem-ber three lions on a shirt,__ Jules Ri - met__ still gleam-ing;_ thir - ty years of hurt__ nev - er stopped me dream - ing.__ I know that was then,__ but it could be a - gain.

It's com-ing home,__ it's com-ing, foot-ball's com-ing home,__ it's com-ing home.__

A♭  E♭/G  Fm  B♭  E♭  E♭/D  Cm  E♭/B♭

It's com- ing home,__ it's com- ing, foot-ball's com-ing home,_____ it's com- ing home._

Three lions on a shirt,___ Jules Ri- met_ still gleam - ing;_

*Repeat to fade*

A♭  E♭/G  Fm  B♭  E♭  E♭/D  Cm  E♭/B♭

It's com- ing home,__ it's com- ing, foot-ball's com-ing home,_____ it's com- ing home._

thir - ty years of hurt___ nev - er stopped me dream - ing._

*Verse 2:*
So many jokes, so many sneers,
But although oh-so-nears
Wear you down
Through the years.
But I still see that tackle by Moore
And when Lineker scored.
Bobby belting the ball
And Nobby dancing.

Any Great British Songbook must naturally feature at least one "pitch-perfect" football song – soccer and pop being two dominant strands in the young British psyche. Various existing songs had already been enlisted as anthems by the fans in the stands, including 'You'll Never Walk Alone' as popularised by Gerry Marsden – but how many of the lads chanting along could have dreamed that it was originally from a Broadway musical by Rodgers & Hammerstein? Thus, it was only a matter of time until football songs were being custom-built in Britain's Tin Pan Alley. The brief: a catchy tune, suitable for a male voice choir of approximately 50,000 voices, and instantly memorable lyrics. Among the most notable: 'Back Home,' written and produced by Bill Martin of 'Congratulations' and 'Puppet On A String' fame, featuring the entire 1970 England World Cup Squad… New Order's 'World In Motion', the England team's single for the 1990 World Cup, in which the national name became a three-syllable word ("Ing-er-land")… and 'Three Lions' with music by Ian Broudie, left, and words by the TV comedians and *Fantasy Football* presenters, David Baddiel, centre, and Frank Skinner, right.

# 1997 Angels

Words & Music by Robbie Williams & Guy Chambers

© Copyright 1997 EMI Virgin Music Limited (50%)/BMG Music Publishing Limited (50%).
All Rights Reserved. International Copyright Secured.

**Steadily** ♩ = 76

1. I sit and wait,___ does an an - gel con-tem- plate___ my fate?_

And do they know the pla-ces where_ we go when we're grey and old?___

'Cause I have been_ told that sal-va-tion lets their wings_ un-fold._

So when I'm ly-ing in my bed, thoughts run-ning through my head, and I feel that love is dead,_

I'm lov-ing an-gels in-stead. And through it all_____ she of-fers me__ pro-tec-

-tion, a lot of love and af-fec-tion whe-ther I'm right or wrong. And down the wa-ter-fall_

_____ wher-ev-er it__ may take_ me, I know that life_ won't break_ me,__ when I come_ to call;

she won't for-sake___ me, I'm lov-ing an-gels in-stead.

2. When I'm feel-ing weak_ and my pain_ walks down_ a one - way street,

I look a-bove and I know_ I'll al - ways be blessed_ with love,_

*and as the feel-ing grows____ she brings flesh to my bones, and*

*when love is dead, I'm lov-ing an-gels in-stead. And through it all____*

**Coda**

*And through it all____ she of-fers me____ pro-tec-tion, a lot of love and af-fec-*

*-tion whe-ther I'm right or wrong. And down the wa-ter-fall____ wher-ev-er it may take*

*____ me, I know that life____ won't break____ me,____ when I come to call; she won't for-sake*

*____ me,____ I'm lov-ing an-gels in-stead.*

Robbie Williams' 'Angels', was released in December 1997. Co-written by Williams and Guy Chambers, it was voted best song of the last twenty-five years by BBC Radio 2 listeners, and received a special award at the Brit Awards in February 2005. Its success also gave Williams' flagging career an enormous boost and proved yet again that a vaguely spiritual title plus a soaring climax sung by someone who can hit the notes always stands a good chance of being a hit. Chambers says that he and Robbie wrote the song in about half and hour on the second day after they met, picking up an incomplete melody line that Williams had begun in Ireland. Robbie Williams, left, & Guy Chambers with Ivor Novello award for 'Angels'. Most Performed Song & Songwriters Of The Year.

# Brimful Of Asha

**With a bounce** ♩ = 112

1, 2. There's danc - ing__ be - hind mov - ie scenes,__ be - hind { the mov - ie scenes.
those mov - ie screens.

Sa - di Ra - ni,}
Ash - a Bhos - le,} she's the one that keeps the dream a - live,__ from the morn - ing past the eve - ning to the

end of the light.__ Brim - ful of Ash - a on the fort - y - 'five.__ Well, it's a brim - ful of Ash - a on the

for - ty - five.__ Brim - ful of Ash - a on the fort - y - five.__ Well, it's a brim - ful of Ash - a on the

**1.** for - ty - five.__ 2. And **2.** for - ty - five.__

Ev' - ry - bod - y needs a bos - om for a pil - low, ev' - ry - bod - y needs a bos - om. Ev' - ry - bod - y needs a bos - om for a pil - low,

ev' - ry - bod - y needs a bos - om: mine's on the for - ty - five.

3. And sing - ing, il - lum - in - ate the main_ streets and the cin - e - ma aisles.__

We don't care a - bout the gov - ern - ment warn - ings, 'bout their pro - mo - tion of the sim - ple life and the

dams they are build - ing. Brim - ful of Ash - a on the fort - y - five.__ Well, it's a brim - ful of Ash - a on the

# 1997 | Never Ever

Words & Music by Shaznay Lewis,
Esmail Jazayeri & Sean Mather
© Copyright 1997 Universal/MCA Music Limited (60%)/
Rickidy Raw Music/BMG Music Publishing Limited
(40%).
All Rights Reserved. International Copyright Secured.

**D.S. al Coda**

**Coda**

the way I'm feel - ing, yeah it just don't feel right.

the way I'm feel - ing, yeah it just don't feel right.

You can tell

Domit3

___ me to ___ my face, _____ you can tell ___ me on ___ the phone. _____ Ooh,

*Repeat ad lib. to fade*

___ you can write it in a let - ter babe, 'cause I real - ly need ___ to know. _____ You can tell ___

*Verse 2:*

I keep searching deep within my soul,

For all the answers, don't wanna hurt no more.

I need peace, got to feel at ease, need to be

Free from pain, go insane, my heart aches.

Sometimes vocabulary runs through my head,

The alphabet runs from A to Z,

Conversations, hesitations in my mind.

You got my conscience asking questions that I can't find,

I'm not crazy,

I'm sure I ain't done nothing wrong

Now I'm just waiting

'Cause I heard this feeling won't last that long.

All Saints projected themselves as a street-wise answer to the Spice Girls, adopting the name of a road in Notting Hill notorious for the availability of drugs. They were, clock wise from top left, Natalie Appleton, Shaznay Lewis, Nicky Appleton and Melanie Blatt.

# 1998

# Babylon

Words & Music by David Gray
© Copyright 1998 Chrysalis Music Limited.
All Rights Reserved. International Copyright Secured.

**Moderately** ♩ = 76

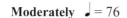

1. Fri-day night_ and I'm go-in' no-where all the lights are chang-in' green_ to red._
*(Verse 2 see block lyrics)*

Turn-in' ov - er T.___ V. stat - ions, sit - u - at - ions run-nin' through_ my_

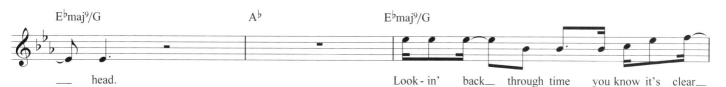

_ head. Look-in' back_ through time you know it's clear_

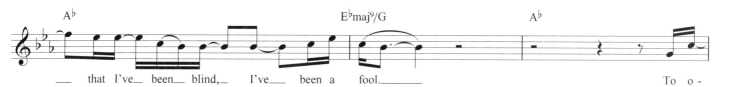

_ that I've_ been_ blind,_ I've_ been a fool. To o-

- pen up_ my heart_ to all_ that jeal-ous-y,_ that bit-ter-ness,_ that_ rid-i-cule.

Sat-ur-day_ I'm run-nin' wild,_ an' all_ the lights_ are chang-in', red_ to green._

Mov-in' through_ the clouds,_ I'm push-in', chem-i-cals_ are rush-in' in_ my_

_ blood-stream. On-ly wish_ that you_ were here,_ you know_ I'm seein'_

*now.*      Let go your heart,___ let go your head___ and feel it___

___ now,_____ Bab - y - lon,___      Bab - y - lon,__

___      Bab - y - lon,_____      Bab - y - lon,__

___      Bab - y - lon,_____      Ah._____

Verse 2:
Sunday all the lights in London,
Shining sky is fading red to blue,
Kickin' through the autumn leaves
And wonderin' where it is you might be going to,
Turnin' back for home,
You know I'm feeling so alone, I can't believe,
Climbin' on the stair I turn around,
To see you smiling there in front of me.

David Gray's 1998 collection *White Ladder* was recorded in his North London house on a four-track machine, and when the album finally became a best-seller it was on the strength of 'Babylon', which became a Top Five single hit. 'Babylon''s success did more than galvanize the slow-burning career of ex-folkie Gray, it stimulated interest in a new acoustic movement and a re-evaluation of the singersongwriter format. *White Ladder* eventually topped the UK charts in August 2001, almost three years after its initial release.

# Why Does It Always Rain On Me?

Words & Music by Fran Healy

...s song from Travis' second album,
...Man Who, was the breakthrough
...that made the Scottish rockers
...nternationally recognised band.
...n Healy's lyric is often taken to be
...ut mental illness and there is
...ainly a strong theme of
...anoia and self-loathing on
...lay.

...e accompanying video
...wed Healy abandoned by the
...d and left bound and gagged in
...boot of a car, which suggests an
...resting interpersonal dynamic
...hin the group that named itself
...r Harry Dean Stanton's character
...e movie Paris, Texas. Perhaps
...dictably, Travis' performance of
...song at the famously soggy 1999
...tonbury Festival triggered an
...ant downpour.

...avis, left to right, Andy Dunlop,
...Healy with Novello Songwriter
...he Year award and Dougie Payne.

Why does it always rain on me?
Even when the sun is shining,
I can't avoid the lightning.
I can't stand myself…

*Verse 2:*
I can't stand myself,
I'm being held up by invisible men.
Still life on a shelf,
When I got my mind on something else.
Sunny days, where have you gone?
I get the strangest feeling you belong.

# Yellow

Words & Music by Guy Berryman,
Jon Buckland, Will Champion &
Chris Martin

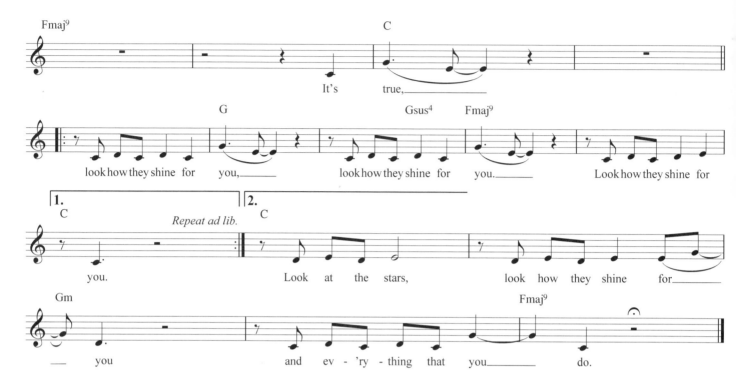

It's    true,_____

look how they shine  for    you,_____    look how they shine  for    you._____    Look how they shine  for

**1.**
C
*Repeat ad lib.*
you.

**2.**
C
Look    at    the    stars,    look    how    they    shine    for_____

Gm
_____    you

Fmaj⁹
and    ev - 'ry - thing    that    you_____    do.

*Verse 2:*
I swam across,
I jumped across for you,
Oh, what a thing to do,
'Cause you were all yellow,
I drew a line,
I drew a line for you.
Oh, what a thing to do,
And it was all yellow.

"'Yellow' refers to the mood of the band," explains Chris Martin of Coldplay. "Brightness and hope and devotion. It's quite concise - you don't have to expand on it. It strikes a chord."

# 2001

# Can't Get You Out Of My Head

Words & Music by Cathy Dennis & Rob Davis

© Copyright 2001 EMI Music Publishing Limited (50%)/
Universal/MCA Music Limited (50%).
All Rights Reserved. International Copyright Secured.

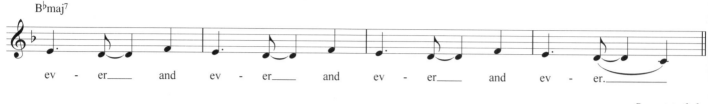

ev - er___ and ev - er___ and ev - er___ and ev - er.___

*Repeat to fade*

La la la, la___ la la la la, la la la, la___ la la la la.

*Bridge 2:*

There's a dark secret in me.
Don't leave me locked in your heart.
Set me free.
Feel the need in me.

# Ev'ry night, every day.

## Just to be there in your arms.

Kylie Minogue (dubbed "The National Thimble" by her fellow-Aussie Clive James) is every inch an honorary Brit. Paul Morley's remarkable book Words And Music (Bloomsbury, 2003) is an extended stream-of-consciousness riff on pop music – and pop culture – inspired by the video for this hit single by Kylie, right. We can do no better than quote from it here, while urging you to read the book itself: "The likelihood is that you will

have heard 'Can't Get You Out Of My Head'; and, whether you like it or hate it, I don't suppose you can get it out of your head. That is a part of its success as an entertainment that verges on a work of art... The song itself is about itself, as well as being about desire, lust, electricity, attraction, movement, appetite, and so on... what makes it a postmodern masterpiece is its ability to combine slick self-awareness with a bouncing strut of

innocence."

Kylie had long ago left Ramsay Street, had graduated from the Stock, Aitken and Waterman Hit Factory, duetted on the dark side with Nick Cave, worn the gold hotpants, flirted with the Pet Shop Boys, and – after 'Spinning Around' – she was back on track as a bonafide superstar... one of the precious few pop stars who needs only a single name (Kylie, Sting, Elton, Cliff) to announce their identity.

# 2001

# Gotta Get Thru This

Words & Music by Daniel Bedingfield

© Copyright 2001 Reverb Music Limited.
All Rights Reserved. International Copyright Secured.

# 2003

# I Believe In A Thing Called Love

Words by Justin Hawkins
Music by Justin Hawkins, Daniel
Hawkins, Ed Graham & Frankie
Poullain

© Copyright 2003 Universal Music Publishing Limited.
All rights in Germany administered by Universal Music
Publ. GmbH.
All Rights Reserved. International Copyright Secured.

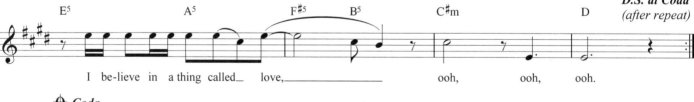

*Verse 2:*
I want to kiss you every minute, every hour, every day,
You've got me in a spin but everything is A.O.K!

The Darkness, left to right, Frankie Poullain, Dan Hawkins, Justin Hawkins and Ed Graham, burst onto the UK scene with this 2003 song written by the band members, and in doing so found that at the start of the 21st century there was still a market for seventies-style glam rock. Combining Queen's overall image with occasional Elton Johntype outsize spectacles and a Bee Gees-style falsetto delivered by lead singer Justin Hawkins, The Darkness might stand accused of being overly derivative, but they went on to win three Brit Awards in 2004, including Best Group, Best Rock Group and Best Album.

My heart's in **overdrive** and you're behind the steering wheel.

Dido

# 2003

# Life For Rent

Words & Music by Dido Armstrong
& Rollo Armstrong

*Verse 2:*
I always thought that I would love to live by the sea,
To travel the world alone and live more simply.
I have no idea what 's happened to that dream,
But as there's really nothing left here to stop me,
It's just a thought, only a thought.

Words & Music by Gary Lightbody,
Jonathan Quinn, Mark McClelland,
Nathan Connolly & Iain Archer

Slow - er,      slow - er,         we don't have___ time___      for that.
*(Repeated chorus see block lyrics)*

All   I want's to find an___   eas   -   ier way      to   get out of our lit - tle___ heads.___

Light up,      light up,         as   if you___ have___   a choice,      ev - en  if you can- not___ hear___

___      my   voice,_         I'll   be right be - side  you___   dear.___

*Verse 3:*
To think I might not see those eyes,
Makes it so hard not to cry,
And as we say our long goodbyes,
I nearly do.

*Repeated Chorus:*
Have heart my dear,
We're bound to be afraid,
Even if it's just for a few days,
Making up for all this mess.

Snow Patrol

# 2004

# Dry Your Eyes

Words & Music by Mike Skinner
© Copyright 2004 Pure Groove Music Limited.
Universal Music Publishing Limited.
All Rights Reserved. International Copyright Secured.

*Verse 1:*

**A**

In one single moment your whole life can turn 'round.
I stand there for a minute staring straight into the ground.

**A/D**

Looking to the left slightly then looking back down.
World feels like it's caved in, proper sorry frown.

**A**

Please let me show you where we could only be just for us.
I can change and I can grow or we could adjust.

**A/D**

The wicked thing about us is we always have trust,
We can even have an open relationship if you must.

**A**

I look at her, she stares almost straight back at me,
But her eyes glaze over like she's looking straight through me.

**D**

Then her eyes must have closed for what seems an eternity.
When they open up she's looking down at her feet.

*(Chorus)*

**Mike Skinner**

The Great British Songbook **327**

**⊕ *Coda*** A

I know in the past__ I've found it hard to say.__

D⁶               E/D    A

Tel-ling you things_ but not tell-ing straight.__     But the more I pull on your

A⁶            D⁶                 E/D

hand and say,__      the more you__ pull a - way.

A

Dry your eyes_ mate, I know it's hard to take_ but her_ mind has_ been made_ up. There's_ plen-ty_    A/D

A                E/G♯

_ more fish_ in the sea.      Dry your eyes mate,__    I know_ you want to make her

F♯m⁷       E       D                  A

see how much this pain hurts.      But you've got to walk_ a - way now.

*Verse 2:*

A
So then I moved my hand up from down by my side,
Shaking, my life was crashing before my eyes.
**A/D**
Turned the palm of my hand up to face the skies,
Touched the bottom of her chin and let out a sigh..
**A**
'Cause I can't imagine my life without you and me,
There's things I can't imagine doing, things I can't imagine seeing.
**A/D**
It weren't supposed to be easy surely?
Please, please I'm begging, please.
**A**
She brings her hands up towards where my hands are rested,
She wraps her fingers 'round mine with the softness she's blessed with.
**D**
She peels away my fingers, looks at me Dnd then gestures,
By pushing my hand away to my chest from hers.

*(Chorus)*

*Verse 3:*

A
Trying to pull her close out of bare desperation,
Put my arms around her, trying to change what she's saying.
**A/D**
Pull my head level with hers so she might engage in,
Look into her eyes to make her listen again..
**A**
I'm not gonna fuckin', just fuckin' leave it all,
'Cause you said it would be forever and that was your vow.
**A/D**
And your gonna let our thing simply crash and fall down,
You're well out of order now, this is well out of town.
**A**
She pulls away, my arms are tightly clamped around her waist,
Gently pushes me back as she looks at me straight.
**D**
Turns around so she's now got her back to my face,
Takes one step forward, looks back, and then walks away.

*(Chorus)*

# 2004 Somewhere Only We Know

Words & Music by Tim Rice-Oxley,
Tom Chaplin & Richard Hughes

aah,_____          oh._____

This__ could be the end of ev-'ry - thing.__ So why don't we__ go

some-where on - ly we know?          Some - where on - ly we know.__

__          Some - where on - ly we know.__

*Verse 2:*

I came across a fallen tree,

I felt the branches of it looking at me.

Is this the place we used to love?

Is this the place that I've been dreaming of?

Keane, left to right, Tom Chaplin, Richard Hughes and Tim Rice-Oxley, produced an instant classic with 'Somewhere Only We Know', as evidenced by covers like the heavenly version on Laura Michelle Kelly's debut album The Storm Inside.

And they went on to win Brit Awards for British Breakthrough Act and Best Album for debut set 'Hopes and Fears' (and, incidentally, to play alongside U2 in America). Keyboard player Tim Rice-Oxley explains the story behind their particular sound: "We used to be a guitar band when we started, and we've been there. But then on my travels I was finding all these gadgets… I realised there was this whole world of sounds that no one had ever really explored. People are so obsessed with guitars, but putting an electric piano into a whole chain of effects and seeing what comes out is something that, as far as I know, no one has ever done before."

Keane took their name from a much-loved child-minder called Cherry Keane: "She was one of those people who really encouraged us to follow our dreams and do the musical stuff we loved rather than worrying about whether we were going to get 'proper' jobs."

# You're Beautiful

Words & Music by Sacha Skarbek,
James Blunt & Amanda Ghost
© Copyright 2004 EMI Music Publishing Limited/
Bucks Music Group Limited.
All Rights Reserved. International Copyright Secured.

There must be an angel with a smile on her face,
when she thought up
# that I should be with you.

The well-documented pop career of ex-army officer James Blunt, above, (né Blount) really took off with this song, which was his third single. Its rise from twelfth position in the UK charts to Number One was no raiding party scramble but rather a measured incursion that took six weeks. Co-written by Blunt with Sacha Skarbek and Amanda Ghost, 'You're Beautiful' went on to invade mainland Europe and finally even infiltrated three separate format charts in the US. On *The Oprah Winfrey Show* Blunt claimed that the lyrics referred to an occasion when he spotted his ex-girlfriend at an underground station with another man.

Girl, put your records on,
tell me your fav'rite song.
You go ahead, let your hair down.

Jools Holland (a fine musician himself, as well as being a Great British champion of fellowmusicians) introduced Corinne Bailey Rae, above,on his show by saying, "A voice so fabulous that after this I will melt. Her songwriting

is utterly glorious, too: wise, intimate, revelatory, inspired. Corinne Bailey Rae's story-so-far provides the perfect note to roundoff our celebration of Great British Song. Her mother is fromYorkshire and her father is West Indian… she started singing at her local

church…
she studied violin at school until her
youth-group leader introduced her to electric guitar… she read English at Leeds University and worked as a coat-check girl in a jazz club, where she met her husband, the sax-player

Jason Rae. Her self-titled debut album entered the UK charts at Number One and within just three months had reached double platinum status.

# Put Your Records On

Words & Music by Corinne
Bailey Rae, John Beck & Steven
Chrisanthou

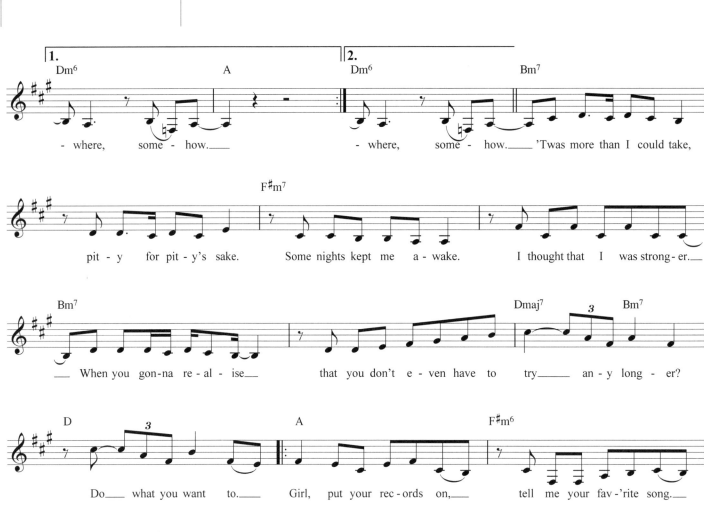

- where, some - how._____                    - where, some - how._____ 'Twas more than I could take,

pit - y for pit - y's sake.        Some nights kept me a - wake.        I thought that I was strong - er._

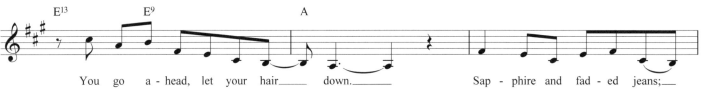

___ When you gon-na re - al - ise___        that you don't e - ven have to        try_____ an - y long - er?

Do___ what you want to.___        Girl, put your rec - ords on,___        tell me your fav -'rite song.

You go a - head, let your hair_____ down._____        Sap - phire and fad - ed jeans;___

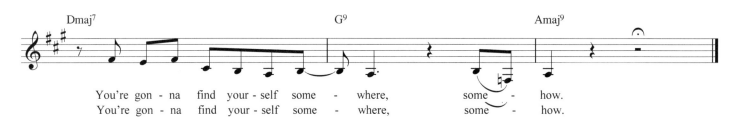

I hope you get your dreams.___        Just go a - head; let your hair_____ down.___

You're gon - na find your-self some - where,        some - how.
You're gon - na find your-self some - where,        some - how.

*Verse 2:*
Blue as the sky, sunburnt and lonely,
Sippin' tea in a bar by the roadside.
Don't you let those other boys fool you,
Gotta love that Afro hairdo.

Maybe sometimes we feel afraid, but it's alright.
The more you stay the same, the more they seem to change.
Don't you think it's strange?

# Dream Catch Me

Words & Music by Crispin Hunt,
Newton Faulkner & Gordon Mills

or else I won't come back at all. See you as a moun-

-tain, a foun-tain, a god. See you as a des - cant soul in the set - ting sun. You as a sound,

just as si - lent as none, I'm yours.

There's a place I go when I'm a - lone, do an-y-thing I want, be an-y-one I wan-

**D.S. al Coda**

-na be. But it is us I see and I can - not be - lieve I'm fall - in'.

**Coda**

or else I won't come back at all.

*Verse 2:*
You do so much that you don't know.
It's true, and I know now who I am.
Yeah, yeah, yeah.
And I know now.

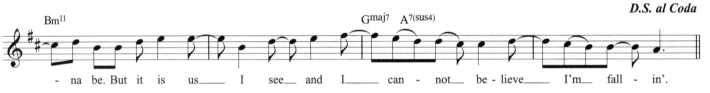

See you as a mountain, a fountain, a god.

See you as a descant soul in the setting sun.

# 2008 | Viva La Vida

Words & Music by Guy Berryman,
Jon Buckland, Will Champion
& Chris Martin
© Copyright 2008 Universal Music Publishing MGB
Limited.

nev - er,   nev - er an hon - est word,___ and that was when I   ruled the world.___

*Verse 2:*
It was the wicked and wild wind,
Blew down the doors to let me in.
Shattered windows and the sound of drums,
People couldn't believe what I'd become.
Revolutionaries wait
For my head on a silver plate,
Just a puppet on a lonely string.
Oh, who would ever want to be king?

*Refrain 2 & 3:*
I hear Jerusalem bells a ringing.
Roman Cavalry choirs are singing.
Be my mirror, my sword, and shield.
My missionaries in a foreign field.
For some reason I can't explain,
I know Saint Peter won't call my name,
Never an honest word,
But that was when I ruled the world.

Coldplay's bid for pop gravitas resulted in this lyrically dense exploration of power won and power lost, redemption vs damnation, a king dethroned and authority challenged. Replete with biblical quotations and chamber music strings, it took its title from an exuberant 1954 painting of watermelons by Mexican artist Frida Kahlo. The Coldplay album on which it first appeared was Viva La Vida or Death and All His Friends and everything from its status in the singles charts (a 'new edit' disqualified it for a time) through its influences, to its inner meaning have prompted earnest discussion among the band's fans. Referencing more art, the official video depicted the band in front of Delacroix's heroic painting Liberty Leading The People. 'Viva La Vida"s success prompted a clutch of plagiarism claims including one from Yusuf Islam and another from Joe Satriani. In general it was very well received and has become one of Coldplay's most popular songs. In 2008 it made the number nine spot in Rolling Stone's annual '100 Best Songs of The Year'. A lone dissenting voice came in the form of Birmingham City football club supporters whose response to its adoption as the team's entrance music during the 2009-2010 season was 'negative', resulting in Coldplay's triumphant exercise in baroque rock being dropped.

# 2009

# Mama Do

Words & Music by Phil Thornalley & Mads Hauge

© Copyright 2008 Universal Music Publishing MGB Limited.
All rights in Germany administered by Musik Edition Discoton GmbH (a division of Universal Music Publishing Group).
All Rights Reserved. International Copyright Secured.

*Verse 2:*
Why should I feel ashamed?
Feeling guilty at the mention of your name.
Here we are again: it's nearly perfect.
What would my mama do?
*(etc.)*

# 2010 She Said

Words & Music by Benjamin Drew,
Eric Appapoulay, Richard Cassell
& Tom Goss

(Mm mm, mm mm, mm mm mm, mm mm, mm.

Mm mm, mm mm, mm mm mm, mm mm, mm.)

1, 3. She said "I love you boy, I love you so."⏜
2. "But I love you boy, I love you so."⏜   She said "I love you ba - by,

oh, oh, oh, oh,_____ oh."_____ (𝄋 Only) Yes she did.__

She said "I love you more than words can say."_   She said "I love you ba -

**To Coda II** ⊕                                **To Coda I** ⊕

-a - a - a - a - by."_____ (2° Only) Oh, yes she did.__

So I said___ "What you're say-ing girl, it can't be right.___

How can you be in love with me?___ We on-ly just met to-night."___

So she said___ "But boy, I loved you from the start.___ When I first heard

'Love Goes Down' some-thing start-ed burn-ing in my heart."___ I said "Stop___ this cra - zy

talk,_____ leave right now and close_ the door."_____ She said

**⊕ Coda I**

So now I'm up in the courts, plead-ing my case from the wit - ness box.
'Cause she likes the sound of my mu - sic, which makes her a fan of my mu - sic.

Tell - ing the judge and the jur - y___ the same thing that I said to the cops
That's why 'Love Goes Down' makes her lose it, 'cause she can't sep - a - rate the man from the mu - sic.

on the day that I got ar - rest - ed "I'm in - no - cent" I pro - test - ed.
And I'm say - ing all this in the stand while my girl___ cries tears in the gal - ler - y.

**1.**

She just feels re - ject - ed, had her heart bro - ken by some-one she's ob - sessed with.

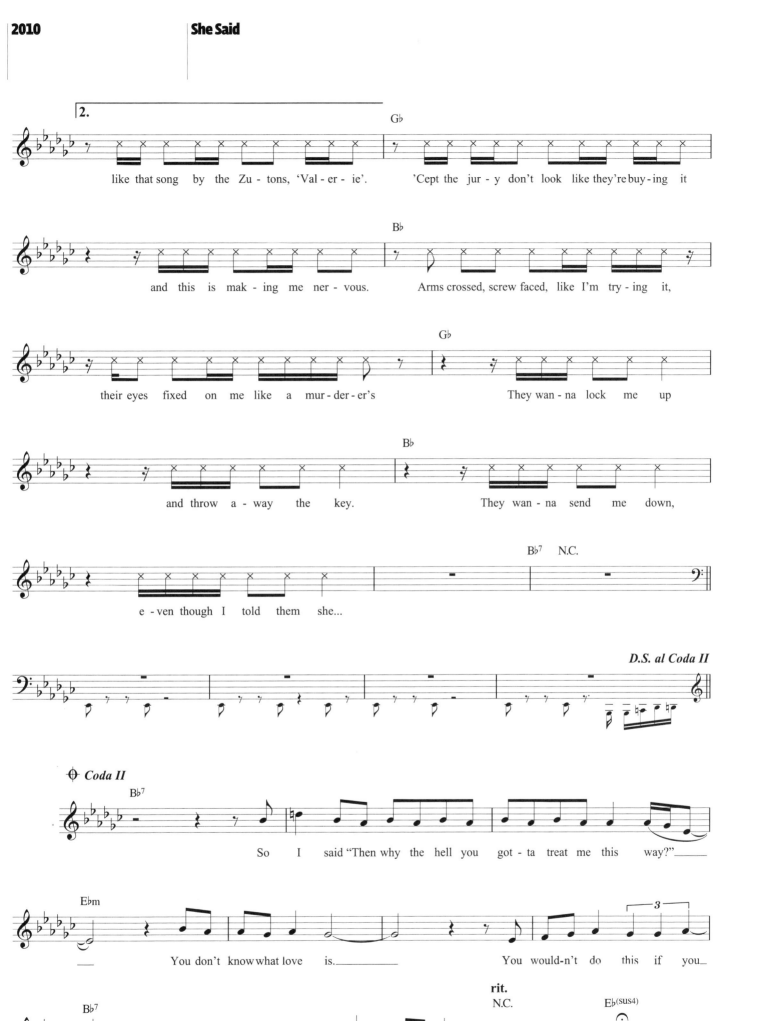

# Someone Like You

Words & Music by Adele Adkins & Daniel Wilson

♩ = 68

A                              C♯m/G♯

1. I_____ heard    that you're    set - tled   down._   That you

*(Verse 2 see block lyrics)*

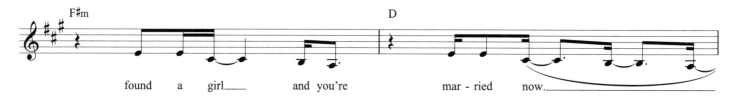

F♯m                              D

found   a   girl___   and you're    mar - ried   now._____

A                              C♯m/G♯

_    I    heard_   that your    dreams   came   true.    Guess   she

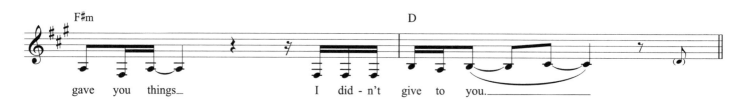

F♯m                              D

gave   you   things_    I   did - n't   give   to   you._____

*1° only*

A                              C♯m/G♯

Old   friend,    why   are   you   so_____   shy?_    Ain't   like

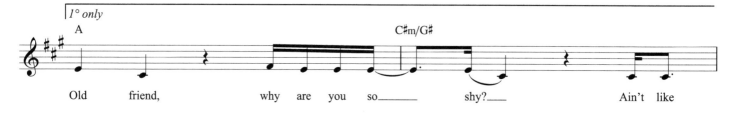

F♯m                              D

you   to   hold_   back,_     or_    hide_____   from the   light._____    I

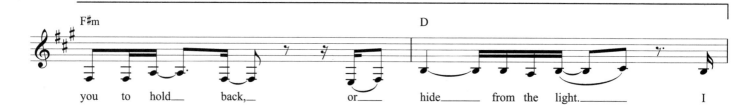

E(add9)                F♯m⁷              D

hate   to   turn   up_   out of the blue   un - in - vit - ed but I_   could-n't stay a - way._   I could-n't fight it.   I had

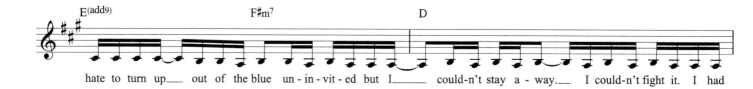

hoped you'd see my face and that you'd be re-mind-ed that for me it is-n't o - ver.____

Nev - er mind____ I'll find____ some-one like____

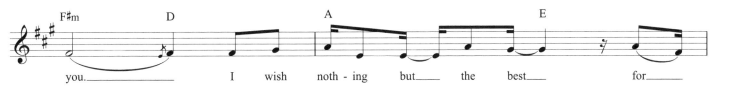

you._____ I wish noth - ing but____ the best____ for____

you two. Don't for - get me, I beg.____ I'll____ re -

- mem - ber____ you said____ some-times it lasts and loves but some-times it hurts in -

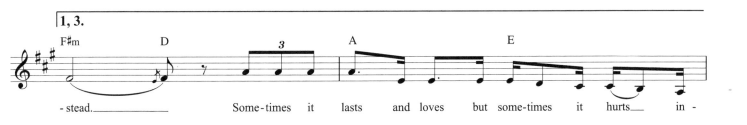

- stead.____ Some-times it lasts and loves but some-times it hurts____ in -

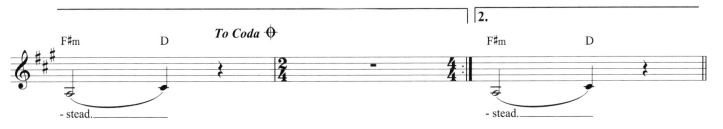

- stead.____  - stead.____

Noth-ing com-pares, no wor-ries or cares, re - grets and mis-takes, they are mem-o-ries made.

*rit.*

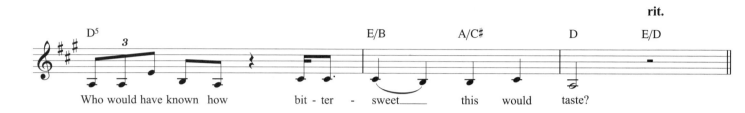

Who would have known how bit - ter - sweet____ this would taste?

**a tempo**

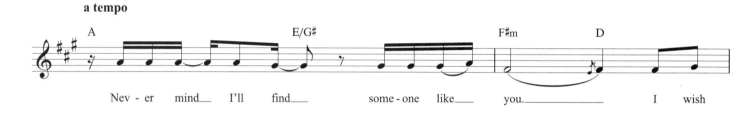

Nev - er mind____ I'll find____ some - one like____ you._____ I wish

noth - ing but____ the best____ for_____ you._____ Don't for -

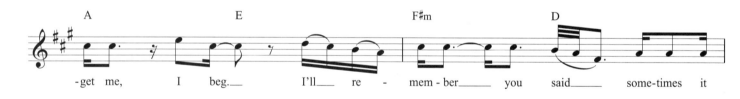

-get me, I beg.____ I'll____ re - mem - ber_____ you said_____ some-times it

*D.S. al Coda*

lasts and loves but some-times it hurts in - stead._____

**⊕ *Coda***

*Verse 2:*
You know how the time flies, only yesterday was the time of our lives.
We were born and raised in a summer haze.
Bound by the surprise of our glory days.
I hate to turn up out of the blue uninvited but I couldn't stay away.
I couldn't fight it.
I had hoped you'd see my face and that you'd be reminded that for me it isn't over.

'Someone Like You' is a prime example of superstar Adele's forte: the pop song as personal therapy. Taken from her 2011 album 21, it supplied the wistful and reflective final track to an album of more or less feisty complaint about an ex-partner who dares to add insult to injury by being happy with someone new. Adele claims to have started writing it with an acoustic guitar, sitting on the end of her bed while suffering from a cold as well as a broken heart and waiting for her bathtub to fill. Somehow she imagined hers to be a unique experience, saying 'I didn't think it would resonate ... with the world!' Before it did she shared the song writing chore with Dan Wilson who also played the piano and produced the track which was recorded at Harmony Studios in West Hollywood, California. Following her performance of the song at the 2011 MTV Video Music Awards, 'Someone Like You' became Adele's second number one single on the Billboard Hot 100, a further milestone in her extraordinary global record-breaking career.

# 2012 | Drunk

Words & Music by Ed Sheeran & Jake Gosling
© Copyright 2011 Sony/ATV Music Publishing/The Movement/BDi Music Ltd.
All Rights Reserved. International Copyright Secured.

♩ = 95

1. I wan - na be drunk when I wake up, on the right side of the wrong

*(Verse 2 see block lyrics)*

bed and nev - er an ex - cuse I made up. Tell you the truth I did what

did-n't kill me, it nev-er made me strong-er at all.

Love will scar your make up. Lips sticks to me, so now I may-be lean back there. I'm sat here

wish-ing I was so - ber. I know I'll nev - er hold you like I used to.

But a house gets cold when you cut the heat - ing.

With-out you to hold I'll be freez - ing. Can't re - ly on my heart to beat in

'cause you take parts of it ev-'ry eve - ning. Take words out of my mouth just from breath-ing. Re-

-place with phra - ses like "When you leav-ing me?" Should I?___ Should I?___

___ May-be I'll___ get drunk_____ a - gain. I'll be drunk_____ a-

- gain, I'll be drunk_____ a - gain to feel a lit - tle

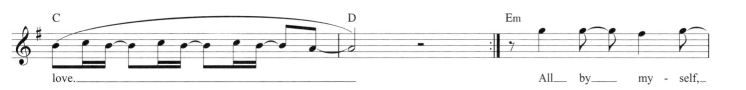

love.___ All___ by___ my - self,___

___ I'm here a - gain. All___ by___ my - self,___ you know I'll nev - er change.

All___ by___ my - self,___ all___ by___ my - self.___ I'm just drunk_____ a-

- gain. I'll be drunk_____ a - gain, I'll be drunk_____ a-

- gain     to feel   a   lit   -   tle    love.

*Verse 2:*

I wanna hold your heart in both hands, not watch it fizzle at the bottom of a Coke can.

And I got no plans for the weekend, so should we speak then?

Keep it between friends, though I know you'll never love me like you used to.

There may be other people like us who see the flicker of a clipper when they light up.

Flames just create us but burns don't heal like before.

And you don't hold me anymore.

On cold days cold plays out like the band's name.

I know I can't heal things with a handshake.

You know I can change, as I began saying.

You cut me wide open like landscape.

Open bottles of beer, but never champagne,

To applaud you with the sound that my hands make.

Should I? Should I? Maybe I'll get drunk again.

I'll be drunk again, I'll be drunk again to feel a little love.

I wanna hold your **heart** in both hands, not watch it fizzle at the bottom of a coke can.

Coldplay's bid for pop gravitas resulted in this lyrically dense exploration of power won and power lost, redemption vs damnation, a king dethroned and authority challenged. Replete with biblical quotations and chamber music strings, it took its title from an exuberant 1954 painting of watermelons by Mexican artist Frida Kahlo. The Coldplay album on which it first appeared was Viva La Vida or Death and All His Friends and everything from its status in the singles charts (a 'new edit' disqualified it for a time) through its influences, to its inner meaning have prompted earnest discussion among the band's fans. Referencing more art, the official video depicted the band in front of Delacroix's heroic painting Liberty Leading The People. 'Viva La Vida''s success prompted a clutch of plagiarism claims including one from Yusuf Islam and another from Joe Satriani. In general it was very well received and has become one of Coldplay's most popular songs. In 2008 it made the number nine spot in Rolling Stone's annual '100 Best Songs of The Year'. A lone dissenting voice came in the form of Birmingham City football club supporters whose response to its adoption as the team's entrance music during the 2009-2010 season was 'negative', resulting in Coldplay's triumphant exercise in baroque rock being dropped.